A Year in the Life...

12 Months of Sewing

Stories by Popser

to JOANNA —
ENJOY !

(Popser)

Open Chain Publishing
Menlo Park, CA

Also by Popser in *A Year in the Life* series:
52 Weeks of Quilting

Cover and illustrations by Chris Hansen
Editing by Elin Thomas and Robbie Fanning
Proofreading by Mora Dewey

First printed October 2000
(Some stories have been reprinted in the *Creative Machine Newsletter*, *Quilt Magazine*, and England's *Popular Patchwork*)

10 9 8 7 6 5 4 3 2 1

Note: The following are trademarked products: Kleenex, Polarfleece, Post-it Notes, Q-tips, Ryder, U-Haul, Velcro

Open Chain Publishing
PO Box 2634
Menlo Park, CA 94026-2634
(650)366-4440 • fax (650)366-4455
www.thecreativemachine.com
info@thecreativemachine.com

Foreword

As publisher of a quarterly sewing/quilting newsletter, I hear often from our readers what they like and dislike. Several years ago, I began to hear about "this guy and his wonderful stories."

His pen name was Popser, and he wrote about his wife's love of sewing, posting the stories on the Internet. People began to forward his stories to me. I, too, was charmed by his amused observations. Not only did they ring true, but they sparked my own memories:

> • The time my sister and I were on a sewing cruise. She walked by me at the sewing machine, paused, and laughed. "You have a piece of monofilament up here," she said. "Ow!" I replied, rubbing the sore spot where she'd plucked a hair. That was a Popser moment.

> • The time I machine-embroidered a baby Monarch butterfly on the seat of my husband's underpants and put them in the middle of the folded pile for him to find someday. Few write about the sly humor released by sewing machines and sewing. Popser does.

His stories also resonated with many other people. They began to read them to their mates, family, and friends. They wrote him fan mail from around the world. Most of all, they begged him to put the stories in book form, so they could share them as gifts, read them as an unfolding story.

While reading, you will laugh, you will commiserate, and you will remember your own stories. Ideally, this book would be published with a blank page across from the end of each story for you to capture your thoughts as a journal or as a letter to others.

Best of all, Momser keeps sewing and Popser keeps writing. You can read his latest stories at http://popser.com.

Robbie Fanning
Editor/Publisher, Creative Machine Newsletter
Co-author, The Complete Book of Machine Quilting

Contents

Introduction

She sat at her new serger and stared at it for an hour. "I'll never be able to do it," she said. She was talking about learning how to use her new serger and getting back to sewing after twenty years, since the children outgrew their need for her to sew for them. But she did learn how to use the serger and, later, a new sewing machine with all its electronic buttons and fancy stitches. During that time, she encountered doubt, frustration, chaos, injury, depression, and she spent a lot of time and money on mistakes she made. But during that same time she experienced creativity, joy, completion, satisfaction, elation, praise from her children and grandchildren, and all the happiness of accomplishment. She discovered that her brain could still work. She went from being what she called, "all thumbs" to being, what I call her, "a sewing wizard."

I began these stories to share her adventures with all those others who have had the same experiences, to commiserate at times and at times to exultate, to sing out what fun it all is. It really has been great fun.

I have been privileged to share her journey through it all, and the following stories reflect what I saw and heard during a year of a sewing life. And, of course, it goes on. I invite you now to share the journey as well.

A.B. Silver
Bakersfield, CA

Note: My thanks to Julie Page who gave me space on her Internet SewingList to first share these stories with so many kindred souls who understand the small agonies and the enormous ecstacies of sewing. And, of course, the absolute inspiration is my wife, Joan, who led the sewing life so bravely during the year of these stories. She did all the real work. All I had to do was write down what happened. She still claims that I embellished the truth a little, but heck, that's what Darling Husbands do.

—ABS

1. Prevention

As the now-sometimes husband of the sewer, I have watched in great awe as my sergermaniac has become a fabricmaniac as well. Our married son and his wife gave my wife a serger for her birthday in December, and then all the world changed. Having three grandchildren who "desperately needed clothes," my wife began behaving strangely. She began sneaking off to the back room, and I began to hear strange noises early in the morning and late at night. Then, the first dawn of understanding came when she said, "I got it threaded. It took only three hours. I got it threaded." Other strange words came out of her mouth: "upper looper, lower looper, cutter, overlock, flatlock, rolled hem." Then the strangest words of all: "I need to go to a fabric shop."

That was weeks ago. Now we have notions and fabric and more notions and more fabric. When, after the shelves of the sewing room were full, I said finally, "Don't you have enough for awhile?" her eyes took on a strange glow and she said, "More."

I, as gently as I could, asked, "*Why?*"

"In case there's a flood or a blizzard and I can't get to the store to get what I need," she answered. "What if we're stuck in the house for days on end? I can't be in the middle of something I am making for our grandchildren and not have what I need to complete it."

Now, that was a strange thing for her to say. Just moments before, in the middle of winter, she had gone out into the sunshine, cut through a balmy seventy-degree temperature, and picked an orange off our very un-snow-covered tree. "We don't have blizzards in this part of California," I said.

"Well, what about an earthquake then?" she smartly retorted.

"It's not likely that you'll be sewing during an earthquake," I replied.

"What do you know? Go download the new Sewing List and meet me at the car. I need some fleece and denim and...."

Help!

But, I have to lovingly admit, our grandchildren do have the cutest capes and robes and jackets and pants and shirts any two-, three-, or four-year-old could ever want. And she can thread the serger very quickly and without the owner's manual.

2. Polarfleece

"Pole police."

"What?" I was startled awake from my sleep by a strange voice.

"Polish Fleas." The voice was disembodied, wandering above the bed. I grabbed at it with what little consciousness I had.

"Who? Where? What?" I asked, thinking I was in my own dream. But my lips were tight and the sounds continued.

"Polished peas." The voice sounded more real now, no longer floating in the eternal ether of our bedroom's outer space.

"Pull our niece."

"Honey, is that you?" this Darling Husband asked, finally recognizing my wife's sleeping voice. I turned and watched her face in the dim red light reflecting off the digital clock. Midnight. Only cats should have been awake singing. Then I saw her lips move, twisted in some kind of demonic anguish. I shook myself awake and then shook her. "Honey, wake up. You're dreaming."

"Polarfleece," she shouted, as she suddenly awakened, her words clear and sharp. She looked to see me, blinked her eyes. "I can't stand it any more. Write to them. Write to them all. Tell them to stop. Please," she pleaded. "Tell them to stop!"

I never wonder long at what she might be thinking, feeling, dreaming, not since the serger popped into our lives, not since she had taken to reading every posting on the Internet, every Internet posting about sewing, not since she subscribed to "The Sewing Pages."

"It's all right, Hon, whatever it is. The dream's over." The nightmare, more likely.

"I dreamed that I opened the sewing newsletters and there were thousands of postings, and every one of them had to do with Polarfleece. Polarfleece this, Polarfleece that. How to find it, how to sew it, how to iron it, how to wash it, whether it pilled, whether it was warm, whether it shrank, how to cut it, how to trim it, how to sew it, how to cook it and turn it into a dish for a hundred people at some sewing banquet."

"Maybe it's an important subject right now," I suggested in my most soothing voice, hoping to calm her.

"It's global warming," she said, her voice suddenly alive. "Yes, that must be it."

"Global warming?" Now, remember, I love this woman.

"CNN," she said.

"CNN?" I repeated, the words a question, but I never question her.

"That's all we see on CNN. The cold weather, the blizzards, the sixty-below chill factor. That's why they need all that Polarfleece. The world is freezing and only Polarfleece will save them."

"Save who?" I asked. "Save whom?" I added, just to be sure.

"All the people stuck in the snow with their sewing machines trying to stay warm, trying to survive the winter." She looked at me now, a plea in her voice. "What should I do? We need to help them."

"We'll go out shopping tomorrow. We'll buy you some Polarfleece." I know my solutions.

She seemed puzzled. "But it's not cold here. It was seventy-eight degrees today. I got a little tan."

"Well, you can make a little jacket for each of your grandchildren and we can send it to them, and if they ever go to Indiana or Ohio or Pennsylvania—" That was enough for her. She smiled.

"Good idea," she said, "Good idea," she repeated more strongly, and I glowed at her happiness and the end of her dread.

She hugged me and smiled again. "Now, go download all those postings," she told me. Her smile deepened. "I need to know where to buy it, how to cut it, how to sew it, whether it shrinks—"

And that's why I'm still at the computer after midnight, waiting to download all the postings about "cola beast"—or was that "popular yeast" or "roller feast"?

3. Colors

We went out shopping the other day to get some matching thread. We went on this quest because not one of the sixty-seven thousand spools of thread she already had neatly lined up in rows on all the free wall space and shelf space left in her sewing room would exactly match the new material our daughter-in-law had bought so my wife could sew a dress for our grandchild—fabric, which as she put it, toddler Rachel picked out herself." (Sewers will understand that last sentence.)

Lilac wouldn't do, nor would purple or heliotrope or plum or puce or grape (Concord) or violet or any other "hue of the short-wave end of the visible spectrum, evoked in the human observer by radiant energy with wavelengths of approximately 380 to 420 nanometers; any of a group of colors, reddish-blue in hue, that may vary in lightness and saturation" (this last, courtesy of the *American Heritage Dictionary*).

I don't know how many sewers or Dear Husbands of sewers who might be found at a display of thread wouldn't be happy with any shade of purple that looked close enough to match. Heck, I bet some wouldn't mind using yellow or white, even if the thread showed, and my wife was planning to set her machine so she could make an "invisible hem." Still—we looked and we looked but no exact match could be found. I tried to persuade her to use a close match. "Here, this looks close enough. No one will know."

"Rachel might know." Rachel, I should say, is two and a half and her favorite color last week was yellow, though the material she had picked out was her new favorite color, and I couldn't name that color even if promised that I wouldn't have to look at a thread display again. I think textile mill managers who make the color decisions clap their hands in glee as they come up with new colors for the new season. I have always suspected, though, that the color is always the same and only the name changes.

"Rachel will believe it is the same color if you tell her it is."

"I wouldn't lie to her."

Would that be so bad? As far as I know, her Crayola box has only one purple crayon. "Then don't tell her. She won't pick up the hem of her dress to check your sewing, let alone what nearly matching color you used."

"She might. She would never trust me again. I could never sew straight again. Guilt would make my fingers tremble and I would twitch all over and probably sew my fingers together in my remorse."

OK, those may not be her exact words. Her exact words might have been more like, "I would feel bad." Maybe I am exaggerating, but I have long ago learned to read all the possible meanings into every word she tells me about sewing. Her emotions, her well-being, her life are hanging by a thread here.

During this conversation she picked up spools of thread, brought them close to her face, glared at each one in scientific endeavor, and put them down again. She brightened with hope, then frowned with dismay as she compared the colors to her sample. "It's no use," she finally said, her head bowed, her shoulders slumped.

"There, there, My Dear," I said. I think I have seen every film ever made where a husband takes a moment to comfort his saddened spouse. In every film, the husband says these magic words, pats her on the back, and the film ends in a romantic look at the moon, as the music tells us all is right with the world. It was no surprise to me that this didn't work with her. No doubt she hadn't seen all the same films.

"Gosh dang it," she said. (Here I am exaggerating. Her comment was much milder, but it carried just as great an impact.) Her face was beginning to take on a shade of purple that matched the fabric sample.

"So, now what?" My old standby question. I had been here before.

"So, there are other shops. We'll go to the Kingdom of Fabrics and Fabric Heaven and Fabrics R Us—" She caught her breath. "And if they are all so stupid as not to have the thread I need, we can go through all the thread catalogs."

"Pleasantly purple," I said in reply.

"What?"

"Vivacious violet or passionate puce," I added. I could probably think of a hundred names for the color her face had just been.

"What?"

"The names of the color you need," I fibbed.

"Perfectly precious plum," she joined in.

Perhaps we lost this first battle, but we hadn't lost the war. Rachel would get her dress made eventually, and every stitch would match the fabric. "Which shop first," I asked taking her hand, "'Fabulously Fragrant Fabrics' or 'Fantastic Fabrics Forever'?"

4. Directions

Help!" she called out. I paid the cry no great attention. As a parent might quickly learn to recognize the screams of a child and know which one is serious and which is not, I have learned to recognize the screams of my wife since she went back to sewing and it became a relaxing madness for her. This scream wasn't asking me to help. It was a scream of frustration. But I lifted myself from my comfortable chair, where I was daydreaming about our upcoming May retirement, and went to see what she was so upset about this time.

"What are you upset about this time?" I asked.

"This #@##$%^%$#@ pattern," she said, as as she rattled the pattern sheet in her clenched fist. "I can't understand it."

"Nonsense," I said sympathetically. She could read and understand anything. She could look at a pattern and follow some of the oddest instructions I have ever seen. I know that the psychologists have said that men are better at spatial relations, that men can read a blueprint better than women, but the research also says that some women can read a blueprint better than most men and that some men can't read the blueprint to draw a straight line. I do know this—when it comes to *my* trying to read a pattern, my head becomes fuzzy, my eyes freeze in place, any idea of what I am doing is lost in the maze of sizes, darts, seamlines, armholes, and grain. *She*, on the other hand, can construct the Taj Mahal from a pattern.

"I can't do it," she said. "Look at this mess." She held a jacket she was making. She showed me the inside of something wrapped around something else attached to something else. She explained that she had just finished sewing in the lining, which was done inside-out, and she was now trying to turn the jacket outside-in to the correct side through a small slit along the seam (about the size of a needle's eye, I thought). It made no sense to me.

"It makes no sense to me," I said. This was empathy.

"It's impossible. If I turn it right-side out, then the sleeves come out backwards."

"Why not leave it that way?" I said. This was compassion.

"Oh, you!" she said, which meant, no doubt, that I would never understand anything about sewing a lined jacket. "Look at this," she said, handing me the pattern which had directions on it for piecing together the jacket.

"And what do you expect me to do with this?" I asked. She knew that I thought it was all gibberish.

"Read it. Maybe you can see what I'm doing wrong."

I wanted to laugh hysterically at the idea of my understanding the directions, but I also wanted to stay alive and, at the same time, show her I was eager to help. "Looks complicated," I said, giving the sheet of directions back to her.

"Read it," she commanded, forcing the pattern on me. I looked at it.

"Hieroglyphics...Sanskrit...cuneiform writing," I mumbled.

"I'm not good enough for something this complicated," she said. "I'll have to do it my way."

"Why don't you do it your way?" I suggested. Her way usually worked better than any other way anyway.

"I'll have to rip it out and start over. Maybe I should go to pattern-reading school?"

"Do they have a pattern-reading school?" I never heard of any.

"Oh, you know what I mean. I'm going to be a failure."

"No, you're not," I said seriously. I was frustrated now. My sweet wife was frowning. I wouldn't allow that. "Let me try reading those directions again."

I peered at them. I read them word for word. I read them upside-down. I read them backwards. I looked for hidden messages. Finally, I came up with something that seemed to say, "Serge, fold, waistline, sleeve, topstitch, inseam, tuck, layers, cut, down, up, sew center, chain shoulder, ruffle overlock, whole grain, measure carefully, add yeast, blend, pour on cookie sheet, bake at three hundred twenty-five degrees for ten minutes."

"Do it your way," I said.

So she did it her way and the jacket came out perfectly, lined and hooded, cute and wearable. She liked it so much she made another two. She embroidered names on them and gave them to the three grandchildren. They were happy. She was ecstatic. I was relieved.

Three weeks later I handed her the daily pile of sewing postings from our lists and she sat down to read them. "Yes! Yes! Yes!" she shouted after five minutes of reading.

"What are you 'yessing' about?" I asked.

"Someone sued the pattern company and won," she said.

"Why did someone sue a pattern company?" I asked.

"For directions that don't make sense. A woman bought expensive fabric and tried to follow the directions on the pattern and the directions were wrong and the fabric was ruined and she sued."

"Great for her," I said.

"Great? Of course great. Now I don't feel so bad. In fact, I feel wonderful."

"Why?" I asked, not that I was unhappy that she felt wonderful. I wanted her to feel wonderful all the time.

"Because it means it wasn't my fault that I couldn't make the jacket come out right. The directions were wrong and I felt I was so foolish that I couldn't understand them and they couldn't have been understood. They were wrong."

"I told you they couldn't be understood," I said. I felt all directions on patterns were written by sadistic company executives who never tried to follow a pattern in their lives.

"Oh, you couldn't follow the directions to draw a straight line," she said, and she began to hum and sing to herself. She was gleeful.

And as for me? I went back to daydreaming about retirement. My directions for that made sense and could easily be followed.

5. Smile on the Crocodile

She came into the bedroom as I lay there in the dark. "Don't turn on the light," I said. It wasn't quite morning, and I was trying to stay in my blanket cocoon. She didn't turn on the light, but she didn't have to. The room was ablaze in light from her smile. I had seen that kind of dawn before. Since she had started using her new sewing machine, our whole house was constantly ablaze with light. "And stop smiling," I said.

She was smiling all the time now. Her cup runneth over once again. If she walked into a table and banged her shin, she might shout out from the pain, but if there was fabric anywhere within her sight, her smile remained. It was getting unbearable. No one should be allowed to smile that much.

"I wasn't smiling," she said, as as she tried to curl her lips downward, but she had little success. The room darkened only a tiny bit and then was bright again.

"I could use you when the power goes out," I said.

"I have a new sewing machine," she said for the hundredth time since we had brought it home.

"Are you sure? Last night there was some frantic knocking on the front door and when I opened it there was a group of ragged people out there who said they were from an organization called Sewing for Humanity and they needed a sewing machine to do their work so I gave them yours."

"You did not," she said, all-knowing, but the light from her smile flickered for a moment before it blinded me again. "Anyway, get up. I want to show you what I can do on the sewing machine." She tugged at the blanket that gave me my security.

"Don't you have to go to the gym?"

"I'm going, but I have to show you something before I go."

"Can't it wait until you come back?" That would give me two more hours of sleep.

"No. Get up!" I got up.

"Put on your glasses," she said. "You'll need your good eyes."

I put on my good eyes. Her smile was even brighter.

She led me into the sewing room over to her sewing machine, her smile a beacon in the dark hallway. "There," she said, as as we reached her new sewing machine.

"There what?" I asked. I was hoping that she was showing me a new place to lie down.

"Sixty-three different stitches," she said.

"Stitches?" I asked, honestly bewildered.

She pointed to a piece of fabric tucked under the presser foot. "I tried out all the stitches on Mine."

"Mine?"

"That's what I call the machine. Mine."

I squinted at the piece of fabric. "Even with my good eyes on, it's hard to see," I said.

She smiled even more widely. If it were Halloween, her smile would win a pumpkin-carving contest. It spread across the sewing machine and spotlighted the fabric and the sixty-three stitches. "There," she said proudly.

"Do you need all those stitches?" I asked. I needed dark and sleep.

"No."

"Then?"

"It's enough that I can do them."

"And you woke me up and blinded me with your silly grin and dragged me in here in the middle of the night so you could show me sixty-three stitches?"

"You would do the same if your computer had sixty-three stitches. Besides, the machine will sew five hundred sixty-seven combinations of those stitches. You're just envious."

"Is there anything else you want to show me?" Please!

"Maybe later. Do you know how many different embroidery patterns there are?"

"Sixty-three?" I suspected I was under by a few.

"Billions," she said. And yes, she smiled.

"How many do you plan to use?" I asked. It was useless to think about going back to sleep now.

"How many do you think?" she asked back.

"All of them."

"Yes!" she said. And she would probably smile at every one of them. Well, I can smile too. I really can. And someday when I've had a good night's sleep, I will. Until then, I'm sure she'll smile for both of us. All I have to do is ask, "Do you have a new sewing machine?"

FeBruary

6. The Break

She took a break today. Two months after she got her serger, four days after she got her new sewing machine, she finally took a break. Miracles can still happen.

"I need some popcorn," she said. "And a fire. I think I'll read a little, too." She had already been reading two months straight. She read every minute she wasn't sewing. Several days before, driving back from visiting our family one hundred fifty miles away in Los Angeles during a heavy downpour and through heavy fog that darkened the sky to blackness, she turned on the map light and read the whole manual for her new sewing machine. For two months she had read serger books, easy-sewing books, sewing-with-your-eyes-shut sewing books, pattern books, catalogs, and all the news on the Internet, domestic and international, that applied to sewing. But she had just moments before finished a little dress for our granddaughter, and she was telling me she needed to take a break. I needed to pinch my arm and my cheek and to step on a tack, all to see if I were dreaming.

It didn't last long. Seven minutes into her book, her popcorn, and the warmth of her fire, she let out a small but shrill yelp. "I just remembered," she said, as as I watched her, wonder and bewilderment both fighting for first place in my head.

"What did you just remember?" I asked, as she stood from where she lay propped up on sofa pillows on the floor in front of the fireplace. She stood and I could almost see that bright light bulb appear above her head. But this was no comic strip. I backed away from where I was standing in the doorway just in case she had remembered something that had to do with sewing. If she was aiming herself toward the sewing room, a collision with her would have made a collision with an eighteen-wheel mile-long truck in the heavy storm days before seem like a pleasure.

"Needle-down," she said.

"What?"

"Needle-down. I just remembered how to set the machine to finish stitching with the needle down automatically." She barely got out the words in one long breath.

"Is that important? I mean why can't it be up? I mean why—?"

There would be no answer from her any time soon. She gave me *that look*, and she began to tighten her body into steel, leaning forward, her head well in front of her shoulders, her slippered feet digging for traction into the carpet. No one else could get traction with the slippers she wore in combination with the Scotch-Guarded surface of the carpet, but determination gave her slippers spikes and turned the rug into an asphalt-covered drag strip. Her mind gave her the green flag. I felt the same breeze the tortoise must have felt the first time the hare rushed by.

"But your break?" I called after her.

"You take it," she said, her voice reverberating down the hallway. Though I felt miles away, I heard the soft click of the switch turn on her sewing machine.

I looked at the fire, the pillows, the cold storm clouds in the sky outside, and I lay down where she had lain and picked up the book she had been reading and dipped my hand into the bowl of popcorn she had been eating. The popcorn wasn't bad, though it needed a little more salt, the fire was cozy, and in a few pages I became interested in the book. I settled in and took only a moment's pause to wonder when she was going to take her next break from sewing. Maybe I should X in a day for her in March or April.

7. Shopping

ad I known even moments before it began, I would never have left home. But how was I supposed to know? The mailer she had thrust in front of my eyes the evening before had simply said, "Sale! One Day Only! 50% Off Everything in the Store."

Still relatively new to this sewing game, we had not yet had a chance to go to a big sale before. Thirty percent off, yes. Forty percent off on notions, yes. But fifty percent off on everything? Who would have dreamed?

We arrived early, as we had planned to be in and out and on our way home before the store became crowded. Hah! As we drove into the parking lot, we looked for but couldn't find the store, yet we had been there before and knew it should have been there. We did see a crowd of people milling around the lot, but we assumed they were customers of the nearby bagel shop. Hah! The crowd, the mob, the population of California were all there, blocking the entrance to the store, all looking at their watches as the minutes ticked down to the eight o'clock opening time. Foolishly, we joined them.

"Stay by me," was the last thing I heard as the doors opened and my wife was swept away by the surge funneling in through the wide open double doors of the entrance. I was pulled along by the crest of a wave of shoppers toward the limited supply of shopping carts in the front of the store. That was when I heard the first scream. The voice came high and shrill. The sounds of three people yelling, "That's my cart," crashed against my ears.

"Let go. Let go," came immediately after.

"I need that cart," said a fourth voice, and the firm, matter-of-fact tone drew my look. A women in red had her two hands on the front of the cart, her fingers welded to the mesh, her face flushed to match her dress as she tugged at the cart. I didn't hear anything after that, as I was pummeled by three women dragging a frightened and bewildered man after them, one pulling, one pushing, the third blocking others out of the way as they headed for the thread display.

Did I say thread display? Oh, no doubt five minutes before there may have been one, but now the display leaned forlornly on its side, the shelves empty, all the thread piled high in a plethora of green plastic baskets toted wildly behind a dozen women jammed into the aisle. I turned to find my wife.

I couldn't see her. I saw what must have been the sight behind Moses during the Exodus. Masses of wall-to-wall people. I tried jumping above the group surrounding me, but all I saw was gridlock, which now blocked all the aisles. With each jump I tried to see my Darling Wife, but it was no use. But then, on the twenty-seventh jump, just when I thought I saw her, I was pulled back down and pushed five or six feet backwards, tangled in arms and legs, and my face was pressed against the groove of what turned out to be the cutting table. My nose found the groove and I came within inches of being cut in half, along with three and one-third yards of yellow calico. Fortunately someone thought my cotton shirt was the end of another bolt of fabric that wasn't yet in anyone else's hands, and I was dragged back to safety. Then I saw her.

"Over here," I yelled. She was caught in a jam by the children's fabric, her body draped in a Batman-covered flannel, her face veiled by a dozen dinosaur appliqué patterns. She freed herself and moved toward me a foot or two before she was dragged back by a woman big enough and strong enough to have four bolts of Bugs Bunny (in a fifty/fifty cotton/polyester blend) under one arm, and she was reaching to grab the bolt of blue denim my wife had pressed like a rifle against her shoulder. But with the yell, "I'll kill you," at the top of her lungs, my wife persuaded the Amazon to release her denim.

"I'm almost there," I said, as as I pushed by a skinny man barely able to hold onto a roll of Wonder Under, his body needing all the extra holding power it could get just to stay in one place against America's hardiest fabric-store shopping fiends.

"Thank God," my normally calm but now sweat-drenched and frantic wife called out hoarsely, as I grabbed her and pulled her to my side. She had the denim in a one-handed steel grip, while in the other she carried a basket full of ribbons and seam binding and needles. ("A new needle for each project," she explained.) In the moment I had before we were both attacked by a wild-eyed woman wielding a rotary cutter slashing her way to the checkout line, I saw that my wife had bought about a billion needles.

"Done shopping?" I asked calmly, as as we followed in the wake of what seemed to be a juggler, a frail and tiny woman in front of us balancing in her hands dozens of rolled remnants that seemed precariously piled ten feet high. Just as she reached the closest and shortest of the three checkout lines, she tripped and fell. The fabric disappeared into a dozen clutching hands and soon disappeared from sight. The woman sat on the floor and wept.

The line was fifteen feet, three shopping carts, and twelve green baskets long. I had plenty of time to count them as we waited. Men and women both stood in line, some swaddled in elastic, some draped in lace, still others decorated by ribbons of silk and satin. As we waited, I had plenty of time to see every item in every cart and every basket and all the items carried loosely, hung over shoulders, clenched between tight teeth.

Thirty-two minutes later we made it to the register. Eighty-seven dollars later (and this was at fifty-percent-off prices) we were free.

"I saw that first. It's mine," was the last thing I heard as we walked out the front doors. Behind us bedlam teamed up with chaos. In the parking lot I could hardly hear the screams anymore.

"I wonder when the next sale is?" my wife asked, as as we piled her treasures into the trunk of our car. She seemed exhilarated.

"Do you really mean that?" I asked, as as I dabbed at the scratches on her face and arms with my handkerchief.

"It'll give you something to write about," she said, catching her breath. She was exhausted but strangely ecstatic. Her need to sew had brought her here today. Her face now glowed from the battle. No doubt she would be back to fight another day.

"Yes, something to write about," I agreed, "and I think I'll call it 'Store Wars.'"

8. Booties

Last weekend we drove two hundred fifty miles to see our son, his wife, and their daughter, our granddaughter. We also went to see their new house. They had moved in the day before and were about to show it off to us. We rang the doorbell and were happily greeted by our son. I started to follow my Darling Wife into the house, but my son stopped us at the threshold. We halted immediately. "Take off your shoes," he said to us.

"Our shoes?" I questioned.

"You have to take off your shoes before you can come in," he said. Darling Wife was already bending down to obey.

I looked down at the shiny new hardwood floors in the house and saw that they were sturdy enough to support me. I dared to take a step. It was a treacherous step. Our son, our flesh and blood, blocked my way. "My shoes are welded to my feet," I said. "Taking them off would take an hour. Besides, my shoes are soft-soled. They wouldn't scratch an itch."

"Dirt," he said. "Off," he said. And for that speech, we sent him to college.

"Go ahead, Hon," my wife said.

"All right," I said, "but I won't like it. My feet are too old to be bare. Feet were made to have shoes. Floors are for walking on with shoes. Get me a chair so I can sit down."

He didn't get me a chair. He held my frail old body while I bent enough to push off the shoes. Later, I knew, I would have to untie them so I could put them on again and then retie them. If I had to go back to the car or go outside for something, I would have to put them on and take them off and put them on and take them off again. Maybe forever.

After a day of walking on hardwood floors and going onto the patio so I could wear holes in my socks, and after stepping on one of my granddaughter's very pointed toys, which felt like it entered my foot and came out my neck, I vowed never to take my shoes off again.

So all this and sore feet led to my wife's decision to save our family relationship by devising a way to keep our shoes on during our future visits. On our trip home, she decided she would make booties to slip over our shoes.

Boy, did she make booties.

"I need a pattern," she said first.

"I could just slip some socks on over my shoes," I said, wanting to prevent her from having to sew something as silly as adult booties.

"You'd have to have very big socks," she replied. "No, I think I'll see what I can do."

I went out to water the lawn and she went to look for a pattern. When I came back into the house, she had a pattern in her hand. "I found the pattern for the nightshirt I made you last winter. It's unisex, and it has a pattern for booties." She was very cheerful.

She went off to her sewing room and I went to watch the news, but I was able to hear only the headlines before she came in waving the pattern. "It's too small. It won't go over your shoes."

"Make it bigger," I said wisely. I knew all the top sewing techniques.

"It's not that simple. I have to experiment. Give me your shoe," she said.

"What?"

"I need something to measure by," she said. "I'll just cut the pattern larger all around, but I'll need your shoe to measure by."

"On my foot or off?" I asked.

"Both," she said, and I found out later she meant exactly that.

And off she went again. Soon, my astute predictions came true. I heard the sounds of sewing drift and rattle and bounce and careen and waft throughout the house. She sighed and hummed and cursed and laughed and yipped with joy before she came back into the living room again.

"How's this for the fabric?" she asked.

"That's all you've done so far?" I asked. I didn't need an answer as I saw her eyes narrow. "The fabric's fine." Navy blue flannel from an old sheet was fine.

And off again she went.

And back. And forth.

Then she had to measure my ankle. She measured it twice. "Are both your ankles the same size?" she asked seriously. She knew from experience that hands and feet and thighs and buttocks and breasts didn't always match. My ankles matched.

And back. And forth.

"Now try this on before I put in the elastic," she said. It fit.

"Do you want it ankle-high or calf-high or knee-high," she asked.

"Ankle's fine," I said.

And back. And forth. And done.

"Try it on," she said. I tried it on. It still fit. "Good," she said. "Now walk around."

I walked around wearing the one bootie (more like a tiny blue flannel tent). I walked on the carpet. It felt fine. But when I walked into the kitchen and took a step, I slid three feet and barely kept my balance. "The flannel's a little slippery on the vinyl," I said.

"Don't take big steps and don't slide and you'll be fine."

I took small steps and didn't slide and I made it across the floor. "Good," she said. "Now take it off. I have to finish the other one."

I sat and pulled at the elastic and easily took off the bootie. It really did work. "This will be great," I said. I looked forward to tromping around that new house. Maybe I would slide through that new house.

"Good," she said again. She held the bootie out in front of her. I could see the light bulb going on in her head. It was at least five thousand watts. "You know, this came out so well, I think I'll make them for everybody. The kids can put up a shelf by the front door and have booties for everyone who visits. I can make hundreds of booties. All kinds of fabrics, all kinds of designs." She stopped a moment in her gleeful momentum and thought a minute. "By the way, do you want me to embroider your name on yours?"

"Why not?" I don't want them to get mixed up with all the others, do I?

9. Maintenance

I don't want to do it," she said. She paced back and forth in the hallway, looking askance at the entrance to her sewing room, sucking in air in tiny breaths of anxiety. Small beads of perspiration began to film her forehead. I felt compassion for her, but what could I do?

She didn't want to do it. I didn't want to do it. But it was time. She knew it. I knew it. It was six AM and the sooner she began, the sooner it would all be over.

"I'd rather have a hangnail," she said. I knew she was serious. "This isn't going be fun," she said. I felt empathy. "Can't we go on a trip or something?" she pleaded.

"It's been too long," I said. Someone had to be firm. She wanted to start sewing on a new project.

"All right. But you will be here, just in case?" she asked.

"I'll be right here," I said. After all, what was a Darling Husband for except to be there in time of great need?

"I'm ready," she said. I nodded in encouragement and she shrugged, shook herself, and turned to go into the room. I was ready. Everything was ready.

"I really hate this," she said in one last moment of doubt.

"You'll do fine," I said.

And she began. She got out the lint brush. She plugged in the vacuum. She hooked up the attachments. She got out the tube of oil. She spread out the dust cloth. She was ready to clean and oil the serger.

Now, there are different ideas about how often to clean and oil the serger. We've read the manuals, asked advice of the dealers and repair people, downloaded tips from the Internet. Some say after every project. Some say every eight hours. Some say when the needle won't move. Some say when mice take up a happy life in the mechanism. Some say never. She decided to clean the machine because she thought it was unhappy. "It looks unhappy," she had said to me the day before. To me, it just looked dirty, but, of course, what do I know?

But inspecting, cleaning, oiling, cleaning, and inspecting again all took time away from her sewing. She believed that in the time it took to clean the machine, she could have sewn up enough clothing to supply the American Red Cross, the Salvation Army, and any other charity that provided aid in the event of a major disaster.

"Bring me the trash can," she said, interrupting my attempt to find the oiling points on the serger.

I turned to see her with a basketball-size pile of lint in her hands. I went out to the yard and brought in a fifty-five-gallon trash can, inserted a giant plastic liner, and watched in awe as she filled it with lint from the serger. "I guess I should have cleaned it more often," she said, as as she clapped her hands to free a cloud of lint that clung to her fingers.

"I guess so," I agreed.

"Now help me with the vacuum," she said. I did, and the huge vacuum, with its hoses that tapered down to the size of a finger tip, roared to life as she cleaned out every nook and cranny on the machine. Soon the canister inside the tank of the vacuum bulged with thread and minuscule pieces of fabric and, from the sound of it, a few broken needles and lost pins.

And so it went. She looked, she poked, she pulled, she sweated, she cursed, she brushed, she vacuumed, she adjusted, she oiled, she screamed now and then, and finally, she was done. She fell into a heap at my feet.

Now, she wasn't alone during this time. No, I stayed by her side, handed her tools, wiped her brow, took her pulse and temperature, brought her cold water to drink, and sang her praises. But she was in charge. It was her machine. It was temperamental. It knew her voice. I would have only been in the way if I got too close.

"I'm done," she said from where she lay at my feet.

"It looks good," I said. "It looks clean."

"Yes," she said with a sigh of satisfaction, "it's a happy serger now."

"Seems to be," I said. What would you have said?

"We'll have to do the sewing machine tomorrow," she said.

"We?" Of course!

10. Resting

She was resting. At first I was worried, for the sounds of the house were gone. Oh, I could hear the hum of the refrigerator, the occasional roar of a neighbor's lawnmower, the caw of our neighborhood crow high on the telephone wire. But there was no sound of sewing. I rushed to her sewing room, but it was empty. Something was wrong. It was two in the afternoon. It was never quiet at two in the afternoon. I think her sewing machine and serger run twenty-four hours a day.

When I found her in bed, a closed book by her side, I thought she was ill. "Are you ill?" I asked.

"I'm just resting," she said.

"Are you sure you're all right? You're not sewing."

"No, I'm just resting. I'm not going to sew for awhile."

I had heard that before. "For how long?" I asked.

"Maybe a week."

"Is something wrong?" I persisted. It seems she had been sewing non-stop for the past two weeks, give or take a few minutes off to eat or sleep or visit our grandchildren. If she used the bathroom, it was to open a sewing magazine or read her manuals.

"Everybody needs a break," she said.

"All right." I was suspicious, but I let her be. She seemed relaxed, but I certainly was not.

I shrugged and tried to throw off the odd feeling I had that her rest wouldn't go on too long. I went to watch the afternoon news, but I couldn't concentrate. I was too anxious. I listened to hear her get up off the bed and storm back into the sewing room, but it didn't happen.

An hour went by. My stomach began to feel queasy. Two hours passed. I stood and paced and cleaned off my desk and downloaded sewing news and tidied up my bookcases. And I waited for her to go to the sewing room. But she didn't go.

At dinner she came and joined me and we ate together as we always did, but she didn't read one page of the sewing posts I left stacked by her plate. We talked of the grandkids, the weather, the news, everything but sewing. "Are you sure nothing's wrong?" I finally asked again. Something terrible must be going on. I felt cold dread as she answered.

"I'm not going to think about sewing for awhile. My brain is full," she said, referring to a comment a student of hers once made.

"I don't believe it," I said, challenging her.

"Well, you'll see."

After dinner I expected her to go to the sewing room, but she fooled me once again. "How about a walk?" she said.

"A walk?"

"It's nice out and it would be fine to go for a walk."

"All right," I said, and we went for a walk.

We walked for an hour, and she seemed quite happy, commenting on the signs of spring, the trees, the flowers, the green, green grass. I couldn't stand it. When we passed a couple of children playing in front of their house, I pointed to them and said, "Look at their cute outfits." She took a look, but it was quick and she turned away.

I was at loose ends. Something was dramatically wrong. I was near panic. This was not my Darling Wife. I was accompanying some stranger.

"There's a sale at the fabric shop tomorrow," I suggested. No dice. "How about the Stretch & Sew demonstration at the Days Inn on Sunday?" I said. No response. "We could go—" I couldn't finish. She had bent to smell pansies in glorious bloom. That was too much.

"You're going home," I said, steering her by the elbow around the corner. I aimed her toward our house. "You're going to sew. I don't care what you sew, but I can't stand you like this."

She was docile, compliant. She followed my lead and we headed back toward the house. "You want me to sew?" she asked with a faint smile curling her lips.

"You need to sew," I said. "You need to," I pleaded. And her smile widened and her eyes brightened.

"*You* want me to sew?" she asked pointedly. I nodded my head vigorously.

"Yes, yes, I want you to sew."

"All right," she said. "If you want me to. But don't ever complain any more that you never see me, that I sew too much, that I'm a sewing maniac or a fabricholic or any of those other clever things you write about me. Remember, you're forcing me to do this—"

She's sewing now. Whatever went on I'm not sure about. I'm sure I'm not going to think about it. I'm going to lie down now. I need a rest.

11. TV News

Three months now into her new life in the sewing world after a twenty-year hiatus, my wife told me today that she really, really likes to sew. "A lot!" she exclaimed as if this were news to me. I could not have imaged that for myself, could I? With her new serger strapped to her life, that emotional tie is as strong as chaining it to her ankle (which she might do if we didn't occasionally have to go out in public to buy groceries—everything else that's important to her she seems to be able to get from her sewing catalogs). And she now does have sewing catalogs for everything. I assume that sometimes during the night she gets on the computer just to expand her database of sewing home pages and news groups and sources for all manner of sewing items. She is so into sewing now that she needs no reminder to think of some immediate project she has to begin or continue or finish. But there are reminders everywhere. For example, Americans are genuinely concerned about what effects television might have on the human mind. I think I can say a little about the subject.

If our television is on and some news commentator mentions any word even remotely sounding like a sewing term, my Darling Wife's ears perk up, her heart beats faster, she smiles a mischievous smile, and she thinks about sewing again. Last night on CBS there was a reference to a financial merger between two giant corporations.

"Are there people who need to finance their sergers?" she asked.

"Merger," I said.

"Oh."

Moments later the news was about flooding in Northern California. There was a human interest story about the rescue of a dog from a raging river. The dog was soon safe but it howled with hunger. Many people volunteered to feed the dog after its ordeal. My wife heard only part of the message. She has proven to be very selective about what she hears.

"I've always wondered why they call it a feed dog," she mused. I didn't correct her. "My old sewing machine needs a new one. We should take care of it tomorrow."

And about some candidate on some election trail, a reporter said, "The candidate seems to have this one sewn up."

"What did he say about sewing?" she asked, as as she looked up from her sewing magazine.

"He said that there was a report from the hospital of an increase in sewing accidents. It seems that more people are getting their fingers caught in their machines because they aren't paying attention." I should have confessed that I was only fibbing, but she would hear me saying that she should buy more ribbing for the six or seven sweatshirts she was working on. Anyway, my words had no effect. She kept on reading. But I heard her give a compassionate sigh.

"Poor things," she said. "I hope their fingers didn't get infected." She hesitated, but only for a brief moment. "Which reminds me," she said, taking me into her confidence. "I need to learn how to take out the stitch finger so I can learn to make a two-thread rolled edge."

Even the weather is on her side. "Tomorrow will be cool and overcast, but no rain is expected," the weatherwoman announced. (I just can't bring myself to say "weatherperson.")

"Overcast? Did she say something about my overcast? How did she know I was working on my overcast?"

When there was a news break interrupting a news break that was interrupting a news break and the announcer said, "We have some breaking news about a pig blinded by the snow and lost in its pen for three hours before the farmer found it frozen," my wife jumped from her chair and headed for the sewing room.

"What's the matter?" I asked, concerned, but I never know where her thoughts may take her—except to the sewing room.

"I just remembered I had to finish learning how to make a blind-ham—I mean hem."

Maybe it's time to get that V-chip everyone is talking about.

12. Graduation Day

I graduated!" I heard her voice reverberate throughout the house. If I had been in another country I still would have heard it. The windows rattled; the doors swayed on their hinges; the walls rocked from the blast of those two words. I jumped as I stood before the quaking mirror in the bathroom, my face well-lathered, my razor inches away from accidentally removing the beard I had worn for the past twenty years. I dashed (and no, it wasn't Santa on the rooftop this beginning of March) toward the sewing room, the only place from which the sound could have originated.

"What in—" I began, as as I looked for some reason for the volume of my wife's scream.

"I graduated," she said again, more softly now, gentle now, and if the volume wasn't in her voice, it was in the shiver of pleasure that rippled her body.

"You graduated over thirty years ago," I said, calm, reasonable.

"No, not that. I graduated in my sewing."

"What do you mean you graduated in your sewing? You're not in any class. You took one lesson last month and you said you couldn't stand how slowly it went."

"I heard the dull," she said. Her voice was joyous.

"You heard what?" First she was insanely loud. Then she made no sense I could discern. Now she was babbling some nonsense. What did sewing do to change a normal woman into what my wife seemed this moment to have become, a lovely but incoherent inhabitant of the Tower of Babel?

But I never wonder long. "I heard the needle," she said.

She was definitely out of any touch with reality, at least the reality I knew. I wondered that moment again, for the thirtieth or fortieth time in the past months since she had taken up sewing, if there were such a thing as a sewer's asylum. If there was none for her, maybe there was one for me. "What sounds do needles make?" I asked in a very normal, if dubious, tone of voice.

"I heard the dull," she said again.

"Would you like a glass of water?" I asked. I looked at her sewing machine and serger to see what she had been working on, to get some clue as to what she was saying. On her new computerized sewing machine was another shirt for our grandson Shea. She had been sewing bugs onto the gold fabric. Just what a five-year-old wants decorating his shirt, a variety of, as he would say, "cool" bugs. "Maybe some hot tea to relax you?" I asked. I really wanted to bring her back from outer space where she was probably riding on a shooting star.

"I heard the clunking," she said.

"You heard the clunking? What clunking?" That at least made some sense. Did she graduate from clunking school?

"The sound dull makes," she said, still cryptic.

"So tell me about your graduation," I asked, trying to bring her back to the reason for her scream of glee minutes before that must have awakened every Emergency Room Technician for miles around.

"I feel like a master," she said.

"You have another master's degree?"

"Just my own degree in sewing. I finally know what they were all saying. And now I can do it." She was firm in her commitment to make things clear to me.

"Now you can do what?" I asked. I was still in command of my cool.

"I can hear when the needle is dull. It makes a clunking sound going through the material."

"You can hear the needle going through the fabric, and you can hear it make a clunking sound when the needle's dull?"

"I just said that," she said. "I didn't believe it when our quilting daughter-in-law said she could hear the sound a dull needle makes. I didn't believe it when some of those people on the Net said they could hear when a needle was dull. But it's true. I heard it."

"So you graduated?" I assumed she would now want a graduation present.

"Yes, I feel I've graduated."

"And so what does that mean?" Was this some turning point in her life, our lives together? I expected a profound graduation speech now. She was my chosen valedictorian.

"It means it's time to change the needle." She looked at me. "What did you think it means? I'll have that tea now."

13. Lint

I began to sneeze about four o'clock. I had planned to watch the news on television, but as soon as I clicked on the television set, I sneezed. Now, generally when I sneeze, I know why I am sneezing. I either have a cold or my allergies begin to act up. I did not have a cold. True, our plum tree is in full blossom with white petals crisp in the March air. True, our city has every type of pollen known to humankind waiting for true spring to be set free to do me in. But my sneeze was explosive, and I kept on sneezing, and I was in the house where no pollen had yet been sniffed. Something else was in the air.

I used a box or two of Kleenex before I found the source of my torture. When I moved toward the kitchen, my sneezing subsided. When I moved toward the back of the house, my sneezing increased. Aha! When I reached the door of *her* sewing room, my nose went into shock. Every sneeze was an explosion followed by my bones crumbling like some cartoon coyote after discovering that dynamite really could explode.

The door to her sewing factory, as I had come to call it, was closed, which was unusual. She didn't like to be confined and usually kept the door open wide where she knew escape was possible if she needed to run from a broken needle or tangled thread. I sneezed again, and my sneeze was as loud as any battering ram. She opened the door. "Ahhhhchhoooooo," I said, my sneeze signaling what I felt was the end of my life.

"Woolly nylon," she said.

"Lint," I said, for when she opened the door, a multicolored cloud of lint filled the room, floating through the air, surrounding her, her body an apparition, some ghostly figure one moment, some angel the next. She was a rainbow of color. The room was suffused with colors, as floating, wafting, fluttering, and all of it, no matter the poetry in motion I saw, all of it was lint.

"I discovered woolly nylon and I'm using it to make the rolled edge on the table cloth," she explained. "I might have used a little too much. I couldn't remember whether it went into the upper looper or the lower looper, and I couldn't find the manual, so I put it in both, and maybe I shouldn't have threaded the needle with it, too." She was speaking to herself in some secret sewing code—not to me. "It does gives off a little lint," she added, every single word an understatement. With every word she spoke, her breath cut a small hole in the variegated air.

"A little lint," I repeated. She moved toward the sewing table, her body cutting a pathway for me to follow. I held my nose and didn't dare take a breath.

"Doesn't it look great?" she asked, as as she held up the edge of the tablecloth to me. I could barely see it through the haze.

I looked. I blinked. I made a mistake and breathed. I sneezed. I watched the tablecloth billow out as my nostrils flared. "It looks great," I sputtered.

"It's the woolly nylon," she said. And she had such a look of pleasure on her lint-speckled face, I had to love this woman. And I would have hugged her, too, but my next sneeze blew me back out of the room. Still, I would be back. When she was done she would call me to bring the vacuum and get to work. After all, it was my tablecloth, too, woolly nylon and all. And I could always get more Kleenex.

14. My Turn

*I*t's my turn," she said. She was staring out the window at the clear blue March sky, the buds on our apricot tree just beginning to open, our winter grass green and plush and glistening after a light rain the day before.

"Your turn for what?" I asked.

"We'll have to go shopping again," she said, somewhat wistfully. She spoke backwards to me, her words reflecting off the window.

"It's your turn to go shopping?" I said, asking for clarification. But I became suspicious and immediately added, "What kind of shopping?"

"Oh, you know," she said demurely, flirtation in her voice. Now I was more than just suspicious. I looked for some nefarious plot.

"Food, fertilizer, new tires, sheets?" I asked.

"Don't you think it's my turn?" she asked, turning my question off and changing the subject back to where she wanted it to go.

"Is there an answer to that question or is it just a rhetorical question?" In my family, tradition requires answering a question with a question. But she is better at it than I am.

"Do you think I would ask you a rhetorical question?"

"Yes, you would," I said. "So?"

"So, it's more of an ethical question, isn't it?" A cloud floated across the sky and blocked the sun a moment before passing by. I felt a cloud float over me.

"My ethics or yours?" I asked. Whatever happened to her wanting to go shopping? I'd be glad to go shopping if I knew what we were going to be shopping for.

"Well," she began, looking for any movement, even a twitch, in my face or body that would tell her what I was thinking. "Would it be too selfish of me if I took a turn and sewed something for myself instead of for the grandkids?"

"Ahhhhh," I said in great philosophical understanding.

"I just feel so guilty." She paused and I could see the frown appear, first on her face and then down her neck to her body. This was some distraught woman I had on my hands. "It's just that I have all these projects planned. I just got the new Kwik•Sew pattern book for toddlers, and I have all that fabric just sitting there with all the notions, and I have every new thread all those nice people on the sewing list recommended—"

"You want to shop for fabric?" When hasn't she wanted to shop for fabric?

"If you think it's not selfish—"

"Too selfish to buy more fabric?"

"To make something for myself?"

"You want to sew something for yourself?"

"I have a pattern for a spring dress—"

"And it's nearly spring?"

"Yes," she said, giving herself a way out. What seemed to me a fragile, twisted, forlorn woman started to turn back into herself, her eyes that moment beginning to blaze with a new fire captured from the bright sun streaming into the room. (And, yes, there were violins playing and birds chirping all around.)

"Go for it," I said. "The grandchildren will understand. They'll have compassion." (What toddlers with enough outfits to last through the twenty-first century wouldn't have compassion for their grandmother?)

"I really think it's my turn—"

"Yes, yes, it is," I chanted, I cheered, I sang. "It is *your* turn."

"And I won't feel bad about it, will I?"

"No, no you won't," I said with full enthusiasm, shouting.

"Then what are you waiting for?" She grabbed my hand. "Let's go shopping."

We went shopping and we came back with several yards of some spring fashion fabric with tiny flowers blooming all over it, and she is right now cutting out her pattern, and I can hear her in her sewing room saying, "It's my turn. Yes, it is." And I know that I'm sure that she's sure that it really is her turn. Don't worry kids, your turn is next.

15. Grand Canyon

rand Canyon."

"That sounds great. When are we leaving?"

"The first week of June." She was enthusiastic. She had never been there before, and it had been thirty years for me.

"Show me on the map," she said. I laid the map of the western states flat on her sewing table and pointed out the highlighted route I had drawn with the yellow felt marker. I traced the route with my finger, pointing at where we would stay the first night.

"Is that a big city?" she asked, as as she pointed to Kingman, Arizona.

"Probably for the people who live there," I said.

"How big?" she persisted.

"How big does it have to be?" I asked. I shouldn't have asked.

"Big enough to have a fabric store?" she said, much too quickly.

"Probably not," I said just as quickly. "There are only about twelve thousand people there. Besides, we're just passing through. It's quite a way beyond that to the Grand Canyon. And if we want to get there before dark, we can't dawdle." (I hoped there was a law against dawdling in Arizona.) "See—" I said, pointing at the map. I became wary as I began to realize the intent of her well-focused scrutiny of our route.

"Is there a bigger city closer to Grand Canyon? What about Flagstaff or Phoenix?"

"They're very, very far away from where we'll be staying."

"How far?" There was that tell-tale mischievous glint in her eye.

"Several hours of hard driving away," I said in my most discouraging voice.

"Well, we should at least go to Flagstaff. It's only a couple of inches away—"

"Those two inches are a hundred miles. That's about three hours of driving. And in summer traffic—" She knew I really hated driving in summer traffic. I expected understanding, if not sympathy.

"Boston," she said softly.

She turned her face from the map and looked at me. I knew that look from when she began a new complicated pattern on her serger.

"Boston?" I asked. Now, if that wasn't another wrong turn in our conversation.

"You didn't think it was too far when we were in New York and you drove all the way up to Boston to visit the computer museum. Wasn't that even farther? And didn't I go along with you?" Gotcha!

"Well, well—" I stammered.

"I want you to check the sewing group," she said in her victory voice.

Did I dare ask why? "Why?" I asked, oh so foolishly.

"All those wonderful people online. They have all those addresses of all the stores everywhere. Ask everyone where the fabric stores are located."

"Those near Grand Canyon?" I asked, well beaten down, vanquished, and, in that moment of loss, I knew what her answer would be.

"All of Arizona—just in case."

16. Sewing Blues

I'm useless," she said, as as she opened the refrigerator, peered inside, and let the door close by itself. She stared at the closed door.

"What do you mean, you're useless?"

"I'll never be good enough," she said. She wiped at her brow and opened the door again. The light reflected off the chrome of the shelves and brightened her otherwise gloomy face.

"Good enough for what?" I asked. I was concerned.

"I was just reading all the postings you downloaded from the lists and those people all know so much," she said. Her tone was cool, but I didn't know if it was made that way by the refrigerated air or the misery she seemed to be projecting.

"You could stop reading them if they depress you," I said, not knowing why they would. She thrived on reading all the sewing chat, the advice, the questions. She was a regular.

"Oh, no, I love reading them. It's just...." She pushed the door closed and turned toward me.

"Just what?"

"Here," she said, as as she went to the counter and picked up a printout of the recent postings. "Read this one."

I read about a weekend trip to a sewing conference, about classes, and advanced sewing techniques. "You want to go to a conference?" I asked.

"No, I could never do that. I'm not good enough."

"Are we back to that?" I had never seen her demean her own ability. I, of course, knew how good she was.

"I keep thinking of all the things these people do, all the skills they have, all the things they make. They're so creative and all I do is make little outfits for the grandkids."

"They're great little outfits," I said. They were.

"But I can't make all the fancy stuff and use the fancy material and fit in with all these great sewers."

"Do you want to?" I asked. She had never before expressed such a wish.

"No, not really. It's just that...."

"It's just that you're overwhelmed by people who really love sewing," I finished for her.

"No, I really love sewing. I just feel I'm not doing enough." She looked to see if I understood her.

"Have you looked at the pile of clothes we're taking down to the kids next week?" I asked. Perhaps she had forgotten that the two hooks on the door of her closet bent under the weight of the clothes she had sewn since the last trip.

"There are a few," she agreed.

"You could start your own department store." I smiled. She smiled.

"Still," she mused, but at least she kept her smile.

"All right. Let's test this out. Come with me." I took her by the hand and led her to the sewing room. "Go look at the dresses and jackets and everything that's making this house tilt toward this room." I pushed her into the sewing room, watched as she moved cautiously to the clothes, and then I hurried across the hall into the bedroom and picked up the telephone. Thank God for Alex Bell, though I doubt that he foresaw what effect his invention would have on my wife's sewing woes. When I connected, I took the telephone into the sewing room.

"Here, it's for you," I said.

"I didn't hear it ring," she puzzled, as as she picked up the telephone. I watched her face go from a look of concern to a grin to a bright smile. I moved out of the room.

Fifteen minutes later she came into the kitchen and opened the refrigerator door. "You want something to eat?" she asked.

"No," I said. "I have some coffee." I held out my cup to her.

"She was so sweet. She said she was wearing her new dress and that she loved me and it was her favorite color."

"She said all that?" I asked.

"She said she wants new purple pants to go with the blouse I made her last time."

"What about all the fancy stuff, the sewing conference, all those posts that depressed you?"

"Oh, that can wait. Maybe some day. In the meantime I have to get more purple fabric to match her blouse. Are you sure you don't want something to eat? Some more coffee?"

"No, my cup's already running over," I said. And for the moment, it was.

APRIL

17. Too Big

*I*t didn't happen. I mean, it almost happened. She finished the outfit she was making for herself. After dozens and dozens of dresses and pants and shirts and capes and jackets for the grandkids, she made herself a spring dress. A dress for "herself." What an odd phrase to use to describe what she had been sewing.

Oh, yes, it had been her turn. And she did manage to repress the guilt she had felt at first at not sewing for the kids. But it was all to no avail. As merrily as she hummed, as the dress began to take shape, as snappy as she became in her conversation, as much as she glowed from some inner core of happiness, it was all a sham, a deceit, an outright lie.

"It's too big," she said, as she tried on the dress.

"Maybe you should have used the petite pattern," I said. "You did tell me the patterns run large." Now, we do have a relationship, and I didn't want to rub it in, but she had asked my advice and I had told her petite when she had asked. I saw her every day and recognized that she was only a dimple of a woman, a wisp of a thing easily tossed about by the wind on a calm day. Though the mirror in her mind reflected back a size twenty, she was only a size four. If she inhaled and tucked in her chin, I would lose sight of her completely.

"It's too big," she repeated, unaware of my musings.

"You could take it in a drop. You know you could make it any size you want." It was slightly too large but billowed out only a tiny bit. I have seen her make a doll dress out of a circus tent. She could do this dress and rub her belly at the same time.

"No, it's just too big." Well, when she repeats something a third time, her mind is made up and there is no way I can change it.

"So you can make another one." I didn't dare add "petite."

"No, no, not now. I have to make the matching dress." She said this to herself, not to me. I was lucky to even hear her, for the words were not meant for me. She was talking to her inner-self, that part of her that took her away from reality and turned her into a super Grandma.

"Matching dress?" I asked.

"For Shira." (Three-year-old Shira, who outshines the sun in her eyes, and that's without the Hubble Space Telescope.)

"And what will it match?"

"The dress, of course."

"The dress you just made?" What other?

"Yes, of course the dress I just made."

"A grandmother and granddaughter matching outfit?" I added. Well, why not?

"No, Dear, not a grandmother and granddaughter matching outfit." She was firm but gentle. "Since the dress doesn't fit me, I'll give it to our lovely daughter. It should just fit her perfectly."

"But you made it for yourself. You can just take it in a little." Of course it was too late and I knew it as I spoke.

"Oh, I can make one for myself later. With a matching dress for Shira, it'll be a lovely mother-daughter outfit and just right for spring. And I just happen to have enough fabric left over, too."

She just happened to have enough fabric left over. She just *happened* to have enough fabric left over. Hah!

18. Hearts

It may have been because I told her I wanted to have a talk with her about her sewing. Our conversations had become limited to types of fabrics, types of threads, types of stabilizers. When I asked her what impact she thought a space station would have on our future, she replied that it might be nice to try sewing with space-age fabrics.

Maybe it was the way I began when I said, "Let's have a heart-to-heart talk about what's been going on around here since you got your fancy new sewing machine."

She looked at me. I watched her brow wrinkle, her cheeks puff out, and then a twinkle appeared in her eyes. Another husband seeing these expressions might consider that his wife was enraptured by the opportunity to have a conversation and listen to everything he had to say. I saw something quite different. Her expressions I had seen before. I knew immediately that something I said had sent her mind off to some Land of Oz and that I would not be seeing her in my presence much longer.

Sure enough. "Later, Dear," she said back to me, as she turned and was soon gone off toward her Emerald City of sewing.

I think I saw her again that day, but I'm not too sure about that. We may have eaten together, we may have gone to sleep together, but reality and imagination sometimes get mixed up in our house.

The next morning as I prepared myself for the day, I went to my dresser for a clean handkerchief. I pulled one from a pile and began to put it into my pocket when I saw a flash of red. I looked at the handkerchief wondering if I had had a nose bleed I didn't remember and had forgotten to put the handkerchief in the wash. But there was no blood. What I saw was a tiny embroidered heart on the handkerchief. How sweet, I thought.

I went to my closet for my white shirt. Another flash of red. Two small red hearts were neatly embroidered on my pocket. How very, very sweet, I thought.

But that was only the beginning. At the kitchen table, as I sat my coffee down next to my plate, I saw red again. The napkin had a row of red hearts along the top edge. I lifted the plate. Red hearts on the place mat. My heart started pounding, my breath became heavy, my appetite was lost as I turned and looked around the kitchen. The dish towel on the counter was a cardiac mosaic. The toaster cover dripped hearts. I wanted to scream.

But I stayed calm. I moved stealthily through the house, caution in every movement. I went back to our bedroom, sneaking past the closed door of the sewing room where the distant hum of her machine vibrated through my head. I looked around. Why hadn't I noticed? The pillow case I had slept on had a large heart made up of tiny little hearts. In the bathroom, a towel I had used just moments before, still damp from drying my face, had a crescent of hearts. I gasped, I moaned, I laughed in my hysteria. She had gone mad again.

I charged into her sewing room, my mouth open, a million words ready and waiting to be thrust at her, but she stopped me cold. "Hi," she said sweetly. "Look what I learned to do." I knew what that meant. Regardless of my intent to strap her into a strait jacket, I knew I had better look if I wanted my future to be a complete one.

So I looked. She was embroidering hearts on my white athletic socks. "Number Thirty-Five," she said.

"What?" I was too busy wondering how I would explain the hearts on my socks to think clearly. Would the neighbors laugh?

"Number Thirty-Five on the sewing machine. It makes a little heart."

"There are hearts all over this house," I said, finally getting my senses back in order.

"I had to practice," she said

"There are hearts everywhere," I repeated.

"Thanks to you. You reminded me yesterday when you said you wanted to have a heart-to-heart talk. Just what did you want to talk about anyway?"

19. Trim

I ruined it," she wailed.

"Ruined what?" I asked, concerned.

"This hat I'm making. The lining doesn't match up and there's a gap, and it's ruined."

I took the hat from her hand and looked at it carefully. "Hmmmm," I said. "Ahhhhh," I said. "Mmmmm," I said.

"What are you grunting about?" she asked, as she grabbed the hat back.

"It looks fine to me."

"Oh, what do you know. I can't give it to Rachel like this."

"Well," I began, knowing how sensitive sewers are in matters of perfection, "what about all that lace you bought? Couldn't you just trim it?" She must have had miles and miles of lace on her shelf. She looked puzzled. "Well, isn't that what trim is for?" I asked wisely.

"It's for decoration," she said, but I could see she was looking the hat over with new interest. "Hmmmm," she said to herself. She was weakening.

"It's for decoration, yes," I agreed, "but it's really to cover up mistakes."

"No, it isn't," she said, but she wasn't pushing it. "Mmmm."

"Think about it," I said. "Remember those houses we visited that were under construction?"

"What about houses?" She ran her fingers carefully over the yellow-flowered lining where it joined the blue denim.

"You made a point of complaining about how badly the house seemed to be put together. You pointed out cracks in the plaster and cabinets out of line with the walls. And I said that they would all be covered up by the trim."

"So?" She was moving toward the shelves where the rolls of lace were.

"So, that's what trim is for, to cover mistakes."

"It's to make things more attractive," she argued.

"Yes, that was great serendipity, that the trim not only covered the mistakes but looked nice, too."

"I'm not so sure."

"All right. Who do you think invented trim?" She didn't answer. She was unrolling white lace. I went on. "It was the cavemen."

"If you say so." She was ready to listen.

"One day an early caveman came out of his cave after a slight earthquake and noticed that there were cracks around the entrance to his cave. He pointed the cracks out to his wife and she told him the cave looked ugly. Now, he wasn't a very talented caveman, but he was smart, so he tried to think of some way to cover the cracks. He remembered finally that he had cut off some branches from the tree in front of his cave the day before, so he gathered them up and arranged them all around the cave. Not only did they hide the cracks, they looked good as well. His wife applauded.

"When his cave neighbors saw what he had done, they all wanted to cover their own cracks. They asked him where he had gotten the branches, and he said he trimmed them from his tree." She leaned forward with interest. "That's why we call them trim."

"You just made that up," she said forcefully. She had unrolled four different sizes of lace.

"And lipstick, too," I added, going strong now. "At about the same time in history, one of the women in the caverhood had chapped lips...."

"Stop right there," she said. "Caverhood?"

"What else would you call it? Anyway, a friend looked at her and said she had a remedy for chapped lips, and she smeared some brown mud over the woman's lips. Not only did the mud work, but the woman suddenly found herself surrounded by admirers who found her and her muddy lips very attractive. Later, someone tried red mud, and that was even more attractive." By this time my Darling Wife was making a noose out of a piece of lace and was approaching me.

"Don't you want to hear about turkey and the first Thanksgiving and why we call all the extras 'trimmings'?" I asked. I didn't wait for an answer. I escaped and lived to tell the tale.

And by the way, our granddaughter will have a beautifully trimmed hat for spring.

20. Survival

I really thought that when we bought the new freezer she was going to use it for the plums and apricots we would pluck from our trees the first week of June. Each year she froze enough fruit to last her at least through the next year. So it was a surprise to me when she spent the past April weekend in the kitchen. In the kitchen! Away from the sewing room! There she was in the kitchen paring and slicing and cutting, the range top covered with pots, the microwave constantly humming, her movements quick and exact and practiced. I stood in awe at the miracle that this woman wrought. In the past three months of sewing, she had not been in the kitchen as long nor had she ever seemed so busy.

While she toiled (and didn't ask for my help), I went and looked in her sewing room. Was the serger broken? No. Was the sewing machine broken? No. Was she out of thread, fabric, notions? No. No. No. Her room looked the same as it always did. What was going on?

"Paper plates," she said to me. "Plastic knives and forks and spoons. And here's the list for everything else," she added. She handed me several sheets of paper.

"You want me to go shopping now?" I was used to doing all the shopping. After all, as a sewing widower I had the time, and she had a lifetime commitment to make more clothes for her grandchildren.

"Why all the paper plates?" I asked. She had put down large, large numbers for everything on the list.

"Just get them," she said. No please, no niceties. "Now," she said firmly.

Being the wonderful guy that she thinks I am, I went. I shopped. I puzzled over some of the items, but I finished off her lists. I filled the trunk and the back seat of the car with plastic bags of "stuff." I drove home.

When I got home and brought everything in, the kitchen was empty. She was gone. I left the packages and went to her sewing room. There she was, standing still, staring at her sewing machine. "Do you have it all?" she said. No smile. No sweet gratitude.

"Yes, but I still don't know why you wanted all those packages of frozen beans and broccoli and cauliflower—" And all the rest, I thought. We could open our own supermarket.

"Survival," she said.

"Whose survival?" She looked healthy to me. I felt fine.

"Mostly yours," she smiled, and it was some wicked smile. "Mine, too," she added, the smile turning soft.

"And you're going to explain all this work, all this food?" I knew she would.

"I have sewing projects to do," she said.

"That's not new."

"Big projects."

"How big?"

"You may not see me for a while."

"I don't see you much now," I said. "At the table for meals. When you come to bed. We pass in the hall now and then. I was thinking of sending you e-mail."

"I won't have any free time for a while."

"You don't have much free time now."

"I'll be too busy to cook for awhile."

"You were doing fine today." Here it comes, I thought.

"I'm making ahead," she said.

"You're making ahead?"

"I'm putting enough food in the freezer for two weeks. All the meals will be labeled. Breakfast, lunch, dinner. I'm marking them all. We can use paper plates so you won't have to wash dishes—"

"Will I ever see you again?" I asked, knowing I shouldn't be asking any more questions.

"They are big, big projects," she said, her words hitting me with the force of Thor's thunder. I understood. I turned quickly and went back to the kitchen and began to put everything away. I had a project now, too—survival.

21. Designing Woman

I am going mad," she said.

"No, you're not," I replied.

"How do you know I'm not? You just sit there all day at your computer and never pay any attention to me, and I'm going mad."

"How are you going mad?" I asked. I wasn't sure "How" was the right word, but it was a beginning.

"Quickly," she answered.

I tried again. "What is causing you to go mad?" I asked.

"All the new fashions. Every day there are new fashions and I can't keep up. It's maddening."

"So fashions are going mad, but you're not?" I was relieved.

"No, but I could be. I'm just going to give up reading the newspapers and magazines and stay away from that fashion show on CNN. I'm going to make myself a muumuu and only wear that the rest of my life."

"They have different designs on the material. All those tropical flowers. Hibiscus, plumeria, torch ginger, bird of paradise...."

"Then I'll make a galabia or a caftan. That's all I need."

"There are different designs and weaves," I said. "You'll also have to decide on short sleeves or long sleeves." I wasn't making it any easier for her.

"Then I'll join some group where the women all wear the same outfit all the time. Just think, I'll always be in fashion."

"The fashion industry has used all those designs already, for street clothes, off-the-rack, as well as high fashion. I've seen them in the boutique advertisements."

"You're not helping."

"I think you look good in anything you wear."

"Do you know how many new designs come out every year?" She looked at me. "Thousands," she answered for herself. "Maybe millions. It's all so useless."

"Design your own clothes," I offered.

"I can't design a new outfit every time I go out." She looked at me as if I were the mad one in the house. "I don't have time to make a new dress every week."

"Why do you need a different design every time you go out? You just said you could get along with just one outfit."

"Well, there are different occasions."

"So you do need different styles of clothing?"

"Yes. No. I don't know. That's why I'm going mad."

"Can't you wear the same thing more than once?"

"And be like you, wearing those same pants and that same shirt every day?"

"I change every day."

"But it's the same-looking outfit. Men can do that. You can wear a wrinkled old T-shirt and the same pants the rest of your life and it doesn't matter." She looked frustrated.

"You have a hundred T-shirts. Every place we've ever been you bought a souvenir T-shirt." Actually, she had only about fifty.

"I can't wear a T-shirt when we go out to dinner or to visit friends or when we go to a show."

"So you have to get something new each time?"

"Not every time. Every once in a while."

"And you want to look good?"

"I don't want to look bad."

"So you have to find something nice?"

"Yes," she said glumly. "Something nice," she repeated slowly.

"And you need to look through all the fashion magazines and the pattern books and watch the style shows?"

"I'm doomed," she said.

"Why don't you go through your closets and see what you already have and maybe with a few alterations and a few changes you can come up with a new wardrobe?" She had clothes stashed away in about a dozen closets (well, at least five).

"Do you think that will work?"

"Yes," I said. I didn't know if anything would work. Still, it was worth a try.

"Will you help?"

"Help?" Now I was in for it.

"Tell me what looks good and what doesn't. Maybe I'll find something I can wear."

"Maybe?" I have watched her go through her closets before to find "something that looks nice." Making peace in the Middle East or Bosnia would be easier.

"You don't want me to go mad, do you?"

"No, of course not."

And so I helped her go through her closets and it took only three days and she found two dresses and a pants suit she could fix up to wear. She is sewing now, whistling happily, as she changes an old outfit into a new designer outfit. It's what she does. As for me, I think I'm going mad.

MAY

22. Snaps

She had started with Velcro and had graduated to buttonholes and buttons, and now she was ready for graduate school. Snaps.

She had an old snap tool hidden in some dusty box in the back of the garage, saved years before from the Salvation Army's collection bin on the off-chance she might sew again some day. Some day had come and after two hours of looking I found it.

"It's no good," she said, when I handed her the heavy tool and a box of snaps. "These are old metal snaps. They'd cut our grandchildren's precious arms and legs to pieces. We need new ones," she said. She could have said that first, saving me from looking, from ripping my shirt, from breathing in ancient dust and sneezing the top of my head off.

"So you want a new one?" I asked logically.

"Of course. This kind is old-fashioned. I've been reading about **new** kinds of snaps and tools," she said matter-of-factly. What other way would she talk about sewing?

"All right," I said. It was her favorite reply from me, the only one I dared give, and she left me smiling as she went back to her sewing room. I sat to read my book.

In just about eighteen minutes, more or less, she came back and handed me a stack of papers. I looked at them. They were printouts from all the lists she subscribed to. In yellow marker she had highlighted every post that had to do with snaps and snap tools. "Figure out which one is the best and order it," she said. I snapped to attention.

Well, there was such a variety of recommendations, it was impossible. "You decide," I finally said, a very courageous act on my part when it comes to following her orders.

"Let's start easy," she said, not arguing. "I like the snap-tape idea." See how easily she made decisions?

We ordered and the snap tape came, something like twenty yards of it, more or less, and she began to learn how to use it.

Now, here's the question: How many uses can you think of for snap tape? Five? Ten? Twenty? Hah! She used up five yards, more or less, on my undershorts (I really don't know why), a dish towel, two handkerchiefs (in case I wanted to snap them together to make one big one), two baby bibs that already had ties, the morning newspaper (so I wouldn't toss the fashion section before she read it), pillowcases (so the pillows wouldn't fall out during a pillow fight, though I didn't look to see if the feathers were snapped together), a set of sheets (so they would never again fall off the bed), and a half-dozen other very odd items too unsuitable even to mention. I suppose I'll be finding snaps for weeks yet. I haven't even looked in the refrigerator.

"All right," she finally said.

"All right what?" I asked.

"I know how to use snaps. Go order some more. I need to make some baby clothes."

"You used them all up?"

She didn't answer for a moment; then she said, "I have just enough left to snap up your mouth. Go order." I ordered.

23. Wear and Tear

When the children and the grandchildren arrived late Friday night for the Mother's Day weekend, my Darling Wife breathed a sigh of relief, covered her sewing machines, put away her notions, and planned a sewing-free weekend dedicated to quiet, relaxation, and spending quality time with the family.

"I can't wait to see how the outfits will fit," she said to me, as we ate breakfast the following morning. The rest of the family were all up early, soon fed, and then eager to see what Grandma had made for Shea and Shira since the last time.

They opened the packages, wrapped as Saturday presents, for there was no other occasion for giving the clothes, and the kids loved opening presents. Everything had to be wrapped as presents. Our daughter supervised the fitting, urging grandkids into and out of each new outfit.

The outfits all fit except for a couple, which the kids would soon grow into. Darling Wife was pleased, the grandkids were pleased, our daughter and son-in-law were pleased, and I was pleased that now, finally, Darling Wife would have a care-free and well-deserved weekend.

That dream of a vacation soon ended. As we cleaned up after breakfast (theirs), as the grandkids transformed the house into a magic kingdom (completely unrelated to that other Magic Kingdom), the first hint that the idea of quiet time was only a fantasy came when our darling daughter smiled, hesitated, smiled some more, and began her "Flattery will get you everywhere" speech.

"The kids love all the clothes you've made them," Darling Daughter began.

"I love sewing for them," my wife said.

"They want to wear only what you make," Darling Daughter said. Her tone gave us no clue at that moment that her words were coded messages.

"I'm so glad," my wife said. She smiled.

"They won't wear anything store-bought any more," Darling Daughter said.

"There's no reason to," my wife said.

"They wear the clothes all the time," Darling Daughter said. "Over and over again."

"Well, they're growing so fast. It's better to wear them than to let them sit and outgrow them before they have a chance to wear them." What a practical answer. Oh, yes!

"And I have to keep the washing machine going all the time because you know how kids are and the clothes get dirty and they want to wear them again right away."

"I remember," Darling Wife said. She seemed to let her eyes glaze over for a moment, as she was remembering our three children and their childhood. Didn't we wear out three washing machines?

"Well, they play so hard and all...." The mother of two of our four grandchildren began. Suddenly my wife perked up. She had broken our daughter's secret code.

"So, what did you bring?" Darling Wife asked in answer to the implied message.

"Just a few things," Daughter said, her voice soft, her cheeks slightly flushed, her smile turned into that kind of smile that can always bring a mother's resolve into ruin. "It won't take you long," she said. "Just a quick stitch or two."

"Hah!" my wife said.

The sewing machine was uncovered and turned on. The notions boxes were opened. The serger was threaded. My wife rolled her shoulders, flexed her muscles, shook herself free of tension, and breathed deeply. She was ready to sew, to fix, repair, renovate, rehabilitate the one or two items that needed "just a quick stitch or two."

"Go watch the grandkids," my wife said to me. "This will take only a minute."

"Darling son-in-law took the kids to the park," I said. "I'll wait for you and then we'll go out for a walk to find them." Did I really expect this all to take only a minute? What kind of fool was I?

"You know how rough the kids all play," our daughter said. She smiled again, as she brought a nylon duffel bag into the room. My first thought was that she had joined the army and was off to boot camp. The duffel was large enough to hold all the clothes my wife had ever sewn for the grandkids. And it seemed that it did.

"Yes, kids can be rough," my wife said.

"And tumble," I said, but neither woman paid me any mind. I watched as our daughter emptied the bag onto the floor, and soon the room seemed knee-deep in dresses and shorts and shirts and skirts and blouses and pants and jackets.

"Do you think you can do anything with them?" Daughter asked, her tone begging.

"Maybe something," Darling Mother/Grandmother said, as she picked up the first pair of shorts and looked at it. She held it up. The backside had been abraded to an almost transparent thinness.

"She squirms a lot when she sits," Daughter explained.

"She sits on sandpaper?" I asked. The shorts looked as if they had been used as a scouring pad. Darling Daughter gave me a look. Darling Wife gave the shorts a look.

"It's not too bad. I'll just reinforce the seams a little and it'll wear like new."

"She's very hard on her clothes," Darling Daughter said. As my wife began sewing, our daughter picked up a pair of her son's shorts. The insides of the legs were worn through. "They like to slide down poles in the park," Darling Daughter explained.

"I'll do what I can," said my marvelously patient, indulgent, kind, and crazy wife.

And she did what she could. The few stitches turned into the output of a dozen clothing manufacturers. The few minutes turned into half the day—a seam here, a tear there, a button loose here, a zipper pulled free there, a pocket ripped here, a waistband stretched out there.

I left them there, my daughter holding the next garment in hand, my wife in sewing heaven, smiling in bliss. And I went for the promised walk—by myself.

When I reached the park, I saw my son-in-law at the playground with the grandkids. Shira was on the swing, her feet pumping away. Shea was sliding down the slide head first. I was still far away, but amidst the shouting and laughing and yelling of the children all over the playground, above the roaring blades of a police helicopter high above, amid the loud warnings of the parents for their children to play nicely, I could hear Shea's shirt begin to rip along the seams as he cascaded down the slide. I could hear the buttons pop off of Shira's blouse.

"Well, they are active kids, and I am proud of them," I said aloud to everyone in the park. "If they're a little rough on their clothes, well, they're a little rough on their clothes." I turned and began the walk back home from the park.

24. Button Bin

Though I wanted to get back to the house, she wanted to spend some time after her Mother's Day brunch stopping at the fabric store, where there was a Mother's Day limited, special, one-day-only sale. It was probably limited to the purchase of bolt ends under six inches or already fused fusible interfacing. However, as I was content from being with a nice family after a nice meal on a nice May morning, I agreed to stop.

On Sundays, the store opened at noon. We arrived at twelve exactly and found no shortage of well-dressed mothers and grandmothers already on their way into the store. After passing a huddle of husbands, who had taken up their waiting poses outside the store, no doubt to talk over their wives' sewing successes, as waiting husbands often do, we followed the cheerful group of sewers into the store.

Now, I would have been happier to stay outside, but this was Mother's Day, so I walked by her side, trying to look interested, trying to hide my impatience, but she saw through me, as she usually did, and noted my restlessness.

"Well, as long as you're here, and you're so eager to get out of here, we can save some time if you help. See if you can find several buttons that match. Blue or red or yellow," she said. "Make sure they're exactly the same," she added. "And don't spend a lot of money," she warned. "Get them out of the button bin."

"What button bin?" I asked. I always make sure to ask. Once when she was the one in a hurry, she asked me to buy a white zipper. I did buy one, a white one as she asked, but she never told me how long it was supposed to be. When I showed her the thirty-six-inch zipper, she told me it was just a tad too long to sew into our grandson's size two-T jacket. I told her she could shorten it by using just one of her

12 Months of Sewing

twelve pairs of specialized scissors, but instead of thanking me for the suggestion, she threatened to shorten me.

She led me by my elbow to the counter where a wicker basket about the size of a baby's cradle sat filled with about a zillion buttons. A sign told us that each button was five cents. She looked into the bin a moment, cried out a cheerful, "Oh, good," and handed me a red button. "Here, find three more like this and maybe some blue and yellow ones the same kind and the same size."

"All right. Yes," I said. Of course, I agreed willingly. That should take me a minute or two and then I would be free to stand out in front of the store with the husbands I had just seen. Sewing husbands have a special camaraderie that is sometimes inexplicable to people whose home is not dominated by a sewing machine and a fabric stash.

I looked into the bin where I saw a rainbow of colors and a myriad of shapes. There were buttons with shanks, two-holed buttons, four-holed buttons, shirt buttons, and coat buttons. But I didn't see a matching red button. So I moved my hand to the bin and pushed a few buttons aside, expecting to find three other red buttons with just that movement. Not just yet. I tried again, dipping my fingers an inch below the surface. No luck. I dug deeper. Nope. I scooped up a large handful, scattering some out of the basket. Embarrassed at my sloppiness, I hurried the orphan buttons back into the bin. I scooped again. And again. I looked around to make sure no one was watching as I tried tipping the whole basket to one side, but several women were watching, and I put the basket down carefully. I grinned an apology.

In that bottomless pit of buttons there had to be a few that matched. I tried harder and harder, my hand a blur of motion. Sweat came creeping out of my skin. I tried harder. I was becoming desperate. I looked around again.

They stared at me, several of them sidling up to the table, trying not to appear curious. Who was this strange man stirring the bin of buttons with his hand?

"What are you doing?" a small woman with an eager smile dared to ask me.

"Just browsing," I answered.

"Oh," she said, pulling the word back between her lips as soon as she spoke.

"It's just that we were wondering...," began a tall woman wearing a vest decorated in buttons.

"Did you make that yourself?" I asked, disarming her before she could continue.

"Yes, yes, I did," she said proudly.

"Very pretty," I said. My right arm was now into the basket of buttons, deep down to my elbow. The woman smiled as if she understood what I was doing and moved away. But it was no use. There probably wasn't a matching button in the whole world. The button bin was just a trap to snare innocent men like me. But I wouldn't surrender. I backed away from the bin, as if to make a diving plunge into the buttons. By now every person in the store seemed to be watching.

Afraid to be seen as a madman, I went instead to a nearby rack where dozens of cards of buttons hung in a neat display. Miracle of miracles! On each card the buttons were all the same color, all the same shape, and all the same size. I found a card of four blue buttons, another with four red buttons, and a third with four yellow buttons. I grabbed them all. I didn't look at the price. I didn't care about the price. I took them to the cash register and paid for them and then ripped the buttons off the cards and put them loose in the bag. I threw the cards away in a convenient trash bin and crumpled the receipt. I went to find my roving spouse. Someday I would tell her about this, but not on Mother's Day.

Fortunately, she was already pushing her cart toward the checkout counter. She had finished her shopping and had the content look only a bargain hunter could possess after a successful hunt. "Did you find some buttons?" she asked.

I held up the bag and shook it. The buttons clicked together. "I've already paid for them. I didn't know how long you'd be and other people wanted to get into the bin," I said. Three women did surround the bin. One woman stared back at me, probably still wondering about that strange man.

"Do they match?" she asked.

"Perfectly," I said.

"Good. I knew you could do it. That bin's such a bargain, isn't it."

"Yes, yes, it is," I agreed. A bargain indeed for a bargain hunter like me.

25. Her Summer Dress

Sometimes we discussed the children and the grandchildren. Sometimes we discussed the daily news. And sometimes we discussed life itself.

"How does this look?" she asked. She had on a light purple cotton jumper she had just completed.

"It looks a little big, but fine."

"What does 'fine' mean?"

"It's fine, but it's a little big on you," I said.

"It's a new pattern," she said.

"For the summer?" I asked.

"I need something to wear around the house."

"Then it's a house dress?"

"No, it's for outside, too."

"So it's a house dress you can wear outside?"

"I can wear it anywhere. All the time."

"Do you plan to do that?"

"It's ninety-nine degrees out right now," she said. "We don't have to go out now, do we?"

"No." It was twenty degrees cooler in the house. The air conditioning was on every day. It was still only the middle of May, but it had been over ninety degrees for more than a week.

"That's why I'm staying inside. Is the dress all right?"

"I said it was. Is it comfortable?"

"It's very comfortable. The one I made yesterday was a little tight. The one I made two days ago was a little stiff. I didn't like the fabric against my skin. The one I made three days ago didn't have pockets. I need pockets."

"You're not going to wear those dresses?"

"No."

"What do you plan to do with them?"

"I'll give them to Goodwill or the Salvation Army."

"But not this one?"

"No, I like this one. Do you like it?"

"It's comfortable. You said so. It's a nice color."

"But it's a little big though fine?"

"Yes," I agreed.

"Then I'll wear it."

"Inside and out?"

"Yes. But I'll need a couple more."

"The same style?"

"Other colors. Maybe blue or rose. Maybe yellow."

"Are you going to do that now?"

"Soon. I might try another pattern as well."

"You don't like this pattern?"

"I like it. But it's a little big."

"You like big in the summer. Keeps you cooler, you told me once."

"Yes. I'm keeping this one. I'll wear it tonight."

"We're having company tonight," I said. She liked to dress for company.

"It's summer company. I can wear this."

"It looks good on you," I said.

"It's comfortable. Maybe yellow," she added.

"Yellow?"

"The one I make tomorrow. Don't you like yellow?"

"I like yellow fine."

"With big pockets."

"Absolutely," I said.

"I'm glad you like this," she said. "I'm going to wear it everywhere."

"It's a good dress for the summer."

"Yes, yes, it is. It's just fine for the summer."

26. Peace Breaks Out

Planning began early Saturday morning. She had only two days to get ready. Monday was her target day, and if she were going to win the battle, she had to be ready and able and all her strategies had to be worked out. The first meeting was at the kitchen table. She mapped out her plans carefully. Never before had she been so finely tuned, so aware, so ready.

What it was, of course, was the Memorial Day Celebration Sale, an idea thought up by a generation of merchants who felt that remembering those who gave so much for our country wasn't enough. No, to make the day complete, there had to be fabric sales along with all the other consumer madness that day. She had been considerate of the holiday before, and though she put out our American flag and remembered the real purpose of the holiday, she also knew that to compete in the sewing world she now lived in, she had to defend our future in her own way. Of course, she had to drag me in on her plans.

The problem was that there are three major fabric stores in our small city, and each had sent an advertisement declaring its sale the biggest and the best yet. One store offered a sale on fabric; the second offered a sale on notions; the third offered a sale on patterns. She wanted them all.

"You have to help me," she said. "This is too big for me alone."

"I'll be glad to help," I said, as I sat by her side at the war table. No other kitchen table had recently been set aside for such a grand purpose.

"Here's my plan," she said. She laid out all the flyers and advertisements regarding the sales. With a yellow marker she highlighted what she wanted to buy. "The problem is that there will be a zillion people competing," she said.

"We've practiced war before," I said encouragingly.

"Those were skirmishes. This is total war," she emphasized. "The stores are a half an hour apart from each other," she mused. "We'll have to take them in order."

I looked at the ads. "We're in luck," I said in a military way. "One sale starts at eight. The others at eight-thirty and nine. We can do it!" I wondered if I needed to wear a uniform.

"The patterns are the big problem. This store has only three pattern books, and no matter how early we go, there will be a dozen people at each book."

"I'm not your general for nothing," I said. If she can be commander-in-chief, I could certainly be a general. "We'll go down there today and you can go through the pattern books and write down the numbers of all the patterns you need. Then on Monday you'll have a head start."

"Great idea," she said. I wondered what kind of medal I would get when it was over. "Now, let's figure out our route and what else we'll need to do."

And that was the way it began. We planned for an hour and carefully wrote down every item she wanted. Giddy with excitement, we talked about our coming victory.

That afternoon, she went down to the closest fabric store and went through the pattern books and came back with her pattern list. That store wasn't having the pattern sale, but it sold the same type of patterns. All's fair in love and war, they say. We were in love and at war.

During the rest of the weekend she cleaned up her shelves, sorted through her pattern boxes, organized her notions. If all went well, she would need a lot of new space. I played my role as well. I filled up the tank of the car with gasoline, emptied the back seat and trunk of accumulated disorder to make room for the spoils, and checked the battery. We couldn't overlook one contingency. One mistake and all might be lost.

We went to sleep Sunday night confident we had planned everything as well as we could.

Monday. Memorial Day. We were up before dawn. We ate a shopper's breakfast, the equivalent of a week's food. We even had coffee with caffeine for the jump start it would give us. Our bodies had to be strong. There was no quitting now.

We left the house. We were on our way. By eight o'clock we were at the first store. We were ready to fight the crowd, to get to our selections, to buy, buy, buy. So was every other living person in town. Or so it seemed. But we were undaunted. We held our shields high, wielded our swords, and fought our way into the store.

All right, I admit, the shields were shopping bags, our swords a check book and charge card, the crowds calm and polite, and we didn't have to fight for a thing. The store had plenty of merchandise on hand and we were in and out in twenty-two minutes. It seemed such a letdown after such a buildup. But we still had two stores to go.

"Something's wrong," she said after we left the second store in even less time. "This is no fun. Everything is too easy. They even had extra check-out lines. What fun is a sale this easy?"

"Well, there's still the last store. You remember what happened there last time," I said, remembering her bruises and scratches.

"Yes, that was some great sale," she said, some joy back in her voice. She was hopeful again. There was still a chance for a warrior's victory and the satisfaction it brought.

And so we went to the third store. Due to a construction detour on the way, we were five minutes late to the opening. It didn't matter. No one blocked our way. The customers, and there were many of them, were quiet and orderly. There was a crowd in front of the pattern drawers, each shopper holding a list of pattern numbers (no doubt their spies stole our idea), but when we approached them, instead of blocking our way, instead of yelling and kicking and gouging out our eyes, they smiled and waved us closer. "Come join the party," they seemed to be saying. Still energized by caffeine, my Darling Wife opened the first drawer, checked the patterns against her list, and found all the patterns she wanted still in stock. She was in total confusion.

And it went on like that. It was madness. She found everything she wanted. She was in utter disbelief. It was impossible. Had civilization come to the stores? Had organization overcome? Had efficiency run rampant? Good grief!

There was no joy in victory. There were no skirmishes, no battles, no wars that day. Maybe that was for the best. Peace had overcome. And what a great memorial that was for all of us.

But there's always the next sale. That's around Father's Day. Now that should be something, shouldn't it? The kitchen table has been cleared. I think she's making plans now.

27. Cold Storage

Having just raked up grass clippings from our lawn, I was thirsty. I opened the refrigerator in search of something cold. We usually keep three bottles of water on the shelf, along with a variety of soft drinks and juice. I wiped the sweat that was running from my brow and dried my hands on my shirt. I reached for the water. There was no water.

"Hon," I yelled toward the back of the house. She would know what had happened to the water. While I waited for her to come running to my aid, I looked for something else to drink. I reached for the small bottle of grape juice toward the back of the top shelf. It was a brand I didn't recognize.

The bottle felt odd, too, and I blinked my eyes to free them of the last drops of sweat that blurred my vision. When I opened my eyes again, I could see I was holding a large spool of purple thread.

"Hon!" I yelled even more desperately than before. I looked back into the refrigerator. The whole top shelf was covered with spools of thread. I knew immediately who was responsible. I didn't know why. I looked some more.

"What now?" she asked. She swept herself around the doorway and came to my side. I showed her the thread.

"Don't leave the door open," she said. She closed it.

"Why is there thread in the refrigerator?" I asked. I couldn't wait to hear the reason.

"To keep it fresh. I told you that a long time ago."

"That was for old cotton thread," I said, remembering the sewing tip someone had posted on the Internet. I wasn't sure it worked or was worth it.

"What's to hurt?" she posed. "A little prevention…."

"Does it make it better to sew?" I asked.

"I don't know yet. I just put it in. Ask me in a week, a month."

"The thread's going to be there a month? What about the food, the drinks, my water?"

"Your water is in the small refrigerator you brought home from school when you retired last week. All the drinks are in there."

I went to the tiny cube refrigerator that sat on the floor in the corner. She was right. Inside was the water and all the drinks. All I had to do was bend down three feet to reach them.

I drank my water and cooled off and decided I was hungry. I trekked over to the real refrigerator to get some cherries. I love cold cherries. Cold cherries could make me feel normal again.

"Where are my cherries?" I asked, as I didn't see them.

"Behind the Solvy," she said, as she wiped a wet rag across the door where I had touched it with my sweaty and grass-stained hands.

"What's Solvy?" I asked without hesitation.

"It's a stabilizer I use for sewing," she said. "One sheet of Solvy to one cup of water," she added when I looked very puzzled. "It needs to be refrigerated."

"What's it look like?" I asked. I wanted to avoid whatever it was.

"In the empty peanut butter jar."

I looked into the depths of the refrigerator. I moved aside the peanut butter jar, which was filled with some odd liquid, and wondered if it really wasn't just some new non-fat diet drink she was trying. I looked for my cherries.

"Anything else in here I should know about?" I asked. I looked for fabric. She always said she needed more space for her stash. Would she? No, she wouldn't. For a moment, though, I thought she might.

"Just don't eat anything you don't recognize," she said.

"I don't recognize anything you make lately," I said, chiding her for attempting to make every new non-fat vegetarian recipe she could find to try out on me. I found the cherries and took a handful. I took a bite of one and bit into the pit. I took it out of my mouth. It wasn't a pit.

"What's this?" I asked, handing her a button-shaped piece of concrete.

"That's a button. I'm trying to make some ceramic buttons."

I looked at her. "In the cherry bowl?" It was a reasonable question.

"I put them in the refrigerator to keep them soft and pliable until I could finish and dry them," she said. "They must have jumped into the cherry bowl."

"Jumped in?" I asked. Well, why not? Who says refrigerators have to be only for food and drink?

"Maybe you can buy me another refrigerator," she said then. "Then I could keep my sewing separate."

It was a reasonable request. Just buy her a sewing refrigerator. Actually, everything that day seemed reasonable. That I then took the whole bowl of cherries and walked quietly out of the kitchen and sat in the living room and ate every one of the cherries and wondered what she was going to do next—that was reasonable, too.

Another refrigerator? Should I even think about it?

JuNE

28. A New Rule

I don't understand this," she said. She wasn't speaking to me. I just happened to be walking past the door to her sewing room. She was talking to all her friends: the sewing machine, the ironing board, the chest full of fabric, her notions, the pattern she held in her hand.

"What don't you understand?" I butted in.

She is never embarrassed to be caught talking to her friends. And she is never embarrassed to tell me what she is doing. She has been sewing too long to be embarrassed about anything having to do with sewing. She even admits it when she "very, very rarely" makes a mistake.

"I don't understand why those people change all the rules," she said.

"Sewing rules?" I think she was born knowing sewing rules, though she always tells me a person is never too experienced to learn something new. Her life is full of searching for sewing tips. I'm not so sure about new rules.

"Pattern rules," she said, apparently breaking down the rules into separate categories.

"They have separate rules for patterns?" I asked.

"All the companies have separate rules. I keep thinking I know them all, but then they change one."

"What did they change today?" I asked. I am always one to be interested in new sewing rules—uh, well, pattern rules.

"They probably changed them a long time ago. I just started using this pattern. It's been in my pattern drawer a while."

I must say that she tends to understate a lot of things when it comes to her sewing. Her pattern drawer is actually two filing cabinets, a dozen crammed-full pattern boxes she bought from Nancy's Notions, and a hundred or so old paper towel tubes rolled with more patterns she had copied from "universal" pattern books she didn't dare cut up or she would have lost the larger sizes she would need for her grandchildren as they grow up.

"I never did it this way before," she said.

"You never did what before?"

"The pattern directions say to hem the legs of the pants before sewing them on."

"Isn't that what you do?" I had watched her hem a lot of pants. They always seemed to come out perfectly.

"No, I hem them after I make them. Otherwise they may be too short or too long."

"Doesn't the pattern tell you what size?"

"Children don't come in regular sizes," she said.

"Ours did," I argued.

"Children don't come in regular size twos or threes or fours. Children have little power in this world. One power they have is to confuse us by being a size two and one-third or size four and fifteen/sixteenths."

"They do that on purpose?" I asked. Clever kids.

"Of course they do. So if the pattern says size three, you can be sure the child will probably be size three and forty-five/forty-sixths."

"That makes it tough to sew for them." I was empathic, sympathetic. I'm never finished learning about the hardships sewers have to go through.

"That's the challenge of sewing," she said. She held up the size eighteen-months pants she was making. One side of each leg was sewn at the outside seam, with the whole pants leg spread out flat. "See this," she said, as she turned the bottom to make the hem. "After I sew the hem, then I sew the inside seams to make the pants leg complete."

"Makes sense to me." Actually it didn't. A lot about sewing doesn't make sense to me, even after she explains it.

"No, it doesn't," she said. "I guess the pattern says to sew it this way because some people don't have a sewing machine that can hem this small a pair of pants after the legs are all sewn. My machine has a free-arm, so I can do it. But if I didn't have my machine, this way would be smarter."

"So the pattern rule is a good one?" I asked.

"I didn't say it was good. I said it was different. I said I didn't understand it before. Now I understand it."

"So how do you feel about it?"

"I feel fine about it. But I just know that the pants won't fit the way they are."

"So, you can shorten them or lengthen them?"

"That's more work. I have other projects to do. I can't spend all my time hemming the same pair of pants."

"So what are you going to do?"

"I going to make a wide hem. That's my rule. If the pants don't fit, the cuffs can be let down or rolled up. That way it should fit for five or ten years. Maybe more."

Now, that's a sewing rule I understand.

29. Power Failure

It has happened to the best of us. In some places it happens more than in others. Sometimes it is an act of God. Sometimes it is a mistake of man. This was the mistake of one man. I found that out the next day.

The city was just resurfacing our streets. They were long overdue to be repaired, and when we got the notice not to park our car on the street, we pulled our car into our driveway and hoped the city would work quickly. We knew what kind of mess we would have for several days from the oiling, the stones, the resurfacing, more oil, more stones, black tire marks on the driveway, and black footsteps on the sidewalks. What we didn't expect was that two blocks away a dump truck would be dropping a slurry of oil and stones, and the driver would not see the power lines above. The uplifted bed of the truck snagged the wires and within seconds dragged down the power lines, the telephone wires, the cable lines, and two telephone poles. We didn't hear the poles hit, and we didn't see the roof of a garage cave in, but I did hear my wife give out a tiny scream, a curse, and a long mutter of frustration. The power had gone out in our house and for several blocks around.

Now, I hate when the power goes out because I then have to reset our clocks: digital clocks in the microwave and oven and bedroom along with the clocks on the TV and VCR and, worst of all, my computer. Of course, as it was ninety-five degrees out, our air-conditioning shut off and we became a bit steamed. Literally. While I felt sorry for myself, I forgot the bigger calamity that was going on. I didn't think about what was happening in my wife's sewing room. Her sewing machine and serger and iron shut down.

"Darn, darn, darn," she said. I think she wanted to say something stronger, but she is a nice woman.

"It'll come back on soon," I said optimistically. The last two power outages had each lasted less than five minutes. But I was no oracle that day. I was no prophet. The power was out for eight hours.

Now, eight hours without lights or air-conditioning or television or the microwave or the electric can opener or my computer were all tragedies that we had lived through before. Before, with a sense of humor and a positive outlook, we survived. But that was then and this was now. The *sewing machines* were down.

"I was making buttonholes," she said to explain her pain. "I won't be able to use the sensor and they'll all be different sizes."

"You can't sew now anyway," I said, though I am sure if she wanted to, she would operate the machine by hand, turning the hand wheel until every stitch was complete. "You can start over when it goes back on." She probably wished she still had the old treadle machine.

"But I'll forget where I was. What if I can't remember what I was doing?"

"Have you ever forgotten before?" I asked. "Weren't you right in the middle of sewing on the sleeves of the baby shirt when we went on vacation and yet you just went right back to it when we came back?"

"You don't understand. I'm in the middle of this now. I have to finish. I have all this energy inside me. I have to sew." She didn't seem to be falling apart yet, but she was pacing, and she held out her hands with her fingers spread out, as if she were feeding fabric under the presser foot.

"You can cut out some patterns," I said to comfort her, to offer her some substitute for her thwarted compulsion.

"I was using electric scissors," she said.

"You have the other scissors. They work without electricity. You just open and close the handles," I said. I just wanted to be helpful.

"It's getting warm in here," she said, referring either to the build-up of heat from a lack of air-conditioning or to another more dangerous build-up of steam in her head.

"We can take your machine to a motel," I said generously. "You can finish sewing, and then we can come home when the power's back on."

"I could buy ten yards of very nice fabric for the money it would cost us at the motel," she said. She was a very practical woman.

"How about reading some sewing news from the Internet?" I asked. Then I remembered the computer was down as well. "Never mind," I added quickly. It was getting warmer yet.

"I don't know why they have to have a power shortage during sewing time," she said, as she comforted the sewing machine. She rubbed her hand over the presser foot and up the side to the spool of thread on top.

"You're always sewing," I answered.

"The power could go off between two and three in the morning," she said. "I wouldn't mind it then," she said sensibly.

"Well, it should come on any minute now," I said. It didn't.

"I'm going to lie down," she said. "Maybe I can take a nap. You can wake me when everything's working."

"That sounds good," I said. She went to lie down. I went outside to commiserate with the neighbors.

Only two neighbors were out working on their lawns.

"The power's out," each of us said, and then because it was much hotter outside than inside, I went back inside the house. She was in the kitchen.

"I thought you were going to take a nap," I said.

"I couldn't sleep. I started to fall asleep, but then I began to have a dream that my sewing machine blew up when the power came back on, so I went to unplug it."

"Are you going to stay up then?"

"Yes," she said. There was no hesitation. No doubt. Whenever that power came back on, she would be ready. She already had that power-sewer look, the glazed eyes, her hands in position, her foot pressing an imaginary pedal to run the machine at full speed.

"I'm going to take a nap then," I said. "Wake me up when the power's back on." I wondered if I could sleep if the temperature reached 120 degrees in the house.

"All right," she said, and several hours later, she did awaken me. Oh, she didn't come to wake me gently with a kiss. No, I woke quickly when I heard her scream of joy followed by the whirring of her machine. I even thought I heard her foot push the pedal through the floor, as the machine hit 100 miles per hour to make up for lost time. But they were good sounds, wonderful sounds. Then the air-conditioning came on, and all was well with the world again.

And lately? Lately, I've been seriously thinking about getting a gas-driven generator to keep in the garage. Just in case.

30. Seasons

"Aren't you going to finish the pillow pocket you were making to keep your scraps in?" I asked. She was slicing bananas to put in the dehydrator.

"It's not sewing season anymore," she said.

"What?" I couldn't believe what she had just said. I ran for a Q-tip and cleaned out my ears.

"It's not sewing season anymore," she repeated. "It's June, and it's a hundred and nine degrees outside and I have to do some drying and freezing."

"Since when are there seasons?" I asked. I knew there were seasons, but not for sewers. Sewers always sewed.

"I sewed all winter when it was cold out and foggy and staying inside the house was much more fun than being outside. Sewing was the best thing to do inside the house."

"What about spring? You sewed all spring and it was nice out and you didn't have to stay inside."

"I had a lot of spring projects to do. New fashions, cooler clothing, pretty spring colors."

"Aren't there summer fashions and summer colors?"

"No," she said. And her voice was firm.

"So how long is the freezing and drying season?"

"When it's over, I'll let you know."

"And you're not going to sew anything?"

"I'm going to sew every day. I have plenty to sew. But it's just not sewing season, so I am not committed. I have to try out new recipes and dry the mangos and file my recipes and cook some new non-fat dishes."

"I don't understand you," I said. "You say you will still be sewing...."

"Sewing's in my blood. Our grandchildren need clothes. But I have other lives as well."

"Other lives? Cooking lives and freezing lives and dehydrating lives?"

"Exactly. Don't you have other lives?"

"Yes, but I don't have seasons."

"Everyone has seasons. You used to tell me about when you were a kid and there was stickball season and punchball season. You said there was comic-book season and bottle-top season and skating season and sledding season. You even quoted Ecclesiastes to justify your seasons."

"There were," I said, "but there was a reason for those seasons."

"What was the reason?"

"I don't remember. They just came along every year."

"Well, sewing season is over until next winter."

"But you'll still sew every day?"

"I'll sew when I have to. But I'm not obsessed with sewing right now."

"You're only obsessed during sewing season?" I think I was getting her message.

"I'm not a fanatic. I just sew a little when I have to."

"During the winter and spring," I said, beginning to understand her now, "you are not obsessed and you are not a fanatic, you just sew twenty-four hours a day when it's sewing season."

"I never sewed twenty-four hours a day," she said. "You're exaggerating again." She was slicing honeydew and laying slices out on the drying trays.

"It seemed like you were always sewing or shopping for sewing or reading for sewing."

"So?"

"So how can you say you are a sane woman when it comes to sewing?"

"Sewers don't have to be sane. We just have to know what season it is."

In a strange way, that made sense to me. "Oh," I replied.

"So let's go out and buy some more fruit. And we need more sugar and ascorbic acid. Freezing and drying season will be over before we know it," she said.

"And then what season will it be?" I asked politely.

"I don't know yet. We'll just wait and see."

I am just hoping that it's a season I can live through. Maybe it will be eating season. All that fruit really does look great.

31. The Beach

We went to the beach yesterday. It was going to be ninety degrees in our town, so we drove two and a half hours to the beach on the Central California Coast. We arrived bright and early and walked along the edge of the surf. She finally had her mind off sewing, I thought. We walked over sand dunes toward some driftwood that lay twisted and tangled on the beach. The waves crushed against rocks and sent seagulls flying before the plumes of foam could reach them. Sandpipers bobbed their heads into the sand, and morning beachcombers greeted us as we passed. It was an ideal Saturday morning and we were one hundred fifty miles away from her sewing machine. I didn't know what was in her head, but I hoped the calm and serene morning made her feel at peace with nature.

Wrong!

"Do you think I could make some kind of wallhanging?" she asked, as she picked up a small piece of golden driftwood and held it in front of her eyes. "I could sew something to attach here to hang down from this piece," she said, as she turned the wood from side to side.

"Look at the way the waves hit the rocks," I said, hoping to distract her from another thought of sewing. If I weren't careful, I could lose her.

She threw the piece of wood to the sand. "We don't have any place to hang it," she said. Whew!

"Isn't it beautiful?" I asked. It was a beautiful morning.

"Could you imagine a quilt that could look like this ocean?" she said.

"You don't quilt," I said quickly.

"Oh, I was thinking of some day," she said wistfully.

"Look how the sun sparkles the foam," I said.

"Yes, it is pretty." She looked up to the bluffs above the beach and beyond the bluffs to a row of houses. "You know, if we lived up there I could have a sewing room that looked out over the ocean all day. Wouldn't that be wonderful?"

"Yes, that would be nice," I said. "But we can't afford to live at the beach and still have enough money for your fabric." Uh-oh, how could I have said that? "We should come here more often," I continued quickly, trying futilely to divert her attention back to the beach and ocean and shore birds. I looked to see where her mind was, but her eyes seemed glazed over, her mind gone sailing.

We walked along the sand in silence. We watched people pick up colored stones that had been tossed smooth onto the beach by the last high tide. I picked up several stones and tossed them out to sea. It was so, so lovely there.

"Oh, look at that," she said, as she bent toward the stones. She pointed down to a small pile of shells circled by several strands of seaweed. I looked where she was looking and saw only debris. She kneeled down and picked something up in her hand and stared down at it.

"What's that?" I asked happily. She was enjoying herself now in her explorations. She was really at the beach now, in body and mind.

"Look at this stitching," she said, holding what looked like the remnant of a shirt, torn and tossed by the sea. She lifted the sodden cloth up to my face. I looked at it. To me it was a scrap of sand-encrusted, sun-bleached rag.

"This is what a pintuck looks like. I'm going to try doing this when we get home."

"Pintuck?" I saw that the shredded white rag had several close rows of raised stitching. "Look at the size of those waves," I said without effect.

"You know, we passed a fabric store back in Morro Bay. I wonder if we could find a pintuck foot there."

"Pintuck foot?" Why was I asking these questions? Why wasn't I talking about crabs and sand and sea lions and kelp? I would even be willing to talk about seagull droppings.

"I'll need one for the sewing machine."

"Where do you think all this water comes from?" I said, pointing out to the vast sea. But it was too late. I only wondered, as we stood there on that amazing beach on that amazing morning with clean fresh air how long it would be before she asked to go back, back one hundred fifty miles, back into the scorching heat of our valley, back to her sewing room with a new pintuck foot.

"I wonder whose shirt this was," she said, as she clutched the tiny scrap of fabric.

"Probably some poor sailor who drowned himself when he realized he didn't have a pintuck foot," I said.

"Oh, now you're being silly again." She looked out at the ocean for a moment. I hoped she was marveling at the size of the universe, at the wonder of nature. Nope! She turned to me, and she said with a disarming smile, "I do wonder what time that fabric store in town opens...."

32. Thanks

My mother, who was a dressmaker and tailor from the age of nine, never liked to accept gifts. From time to time, when anyone in the family gave her a present of any kind, she took it only reluctantly and then within a week passed it along to someone else in the family. It came to the point that if anyone wanted something, he or she had only to buy it for my mother and there would be a guaranteed return of the item within hours or days.

My mother was very generous, but she occasionally did deprive family members of the pleasure of giving gifts. I often threatened her if she refused a gift. Once, when she was seventy years old and refused an offer of flowers for Mother's Day, I told her that if she didn't take them and put them in water and display them on her kitchen table, I would punch her in the nose. It was an idle threat, but she did accept the flowers. A brief victory was mine.

Now, I relate all this because my mother complained often of other people who were what she called "ingrates," "unappreciative," "ungrateful" for favors she bestowed upon them. My mother spent her life sewing for other people, and nothing hurt her more, pained her more, depressed her more than people who asked her for a favor and then dismissed her efforts.

"Mom, don't get an ulcer over this," I told her often. I told her this when she spent hours altering a dress for a neighbor, repairing a ripped seam for the grocer across the street, making gifts of skirts and dresses to friends and relatives. Oh, the majority welcomed her help, praised her abilities with a needle and thread, and wore the clothes proudly. But the few who didn't could make her cry out in dismay.

"She's not worth it," I told her when a neighbor picked up a pleated skirt my mother had made as a gift only to complain that the pleats were too narrow or too wide.

"He's nobody you should care about," I said when the young teen-ager who lived next door grabbed the shirt my mother had repaired and walked away without a word of thanks.

"Don't sew for her again," I said when a cousin said the dress my mother made for her five-year-old had the wrong color fabric that didn't match up properly with the daughter's complexion.

But my mother kept on trying to please. She sewed all day long to make money to help my father support our family, but when she sewed in the evening as a favor for someone, she kept her optimism perpetually intact in the hope that her work would be appreciated. And most of the time it was. My mother's great pleasure, outside of being our mother and my father's wife, was to sew for pleasure, not money, and to have that work appreciated.

I told all this to my wife recently when she was smiling with joy at our grandchildren's glee as they tried on their new outfits.

"I keep talking to people who stopped sewing for their kids or grandkids because what they did wasn't appreciated," she said.

"I agree," I said. "And the Net is full of comments about people who don't appreciate all the work that goes into being a sewing friend," I added.

"'Just sew up this outfit for me, won't you? It'll only take a minute,'" she quoted.

"And there's no thanks, sometimes even a complaint that it took too long," I said, having heard or read that a dozen times myself from sewers.

"Some people just tell them that they would be glad to sew on a button or replace a zipper or lower a hem, but that it will cost ten dollars an hour for their time," she laughed. "I'd charge twenty-five dollars," she said.

"What do you say when someone asks you to sew for them?" I asked.

"I always tell them I sew only for our grandchildren. That usually stops them."

"But you would help out someone who asked you?" I asked.

"No, I think I'd let them know that I was too busy with my own sewing or that I wasn't good enough or I would recommend a dressmaker I know. I never want sewing to be work," she said. "It has to be creative and fun and appreciated."

"I wonder how many others feel the way you do?" I asked.

"Most people who sew are appreciated. But there are always a few who want something for nothing, who think they're doing you a favor by asking."

"You remember how hard it was to give my mother a gift?" I asked her.

"Of course. She put up a fuss, saying she didn't need anything, but she let us know she loved us for it. She once told me it was more fun giving than getting, but I told her she had to let us give as well. And she never asked for favors without showing how grateful she was.

"Remember when she made me that green summer dress?" she said. I remembered. It had been within weeks of our meeting each other.

"It was when I brought you home for the first time. I still remember how pleased you were with it," I said. "It made you feel part of the family. And I also remember how pleased I was about how good you looked in it. My mother was very happy you liked it so much."

"I really liked getting that dress, though I didn't really like green. I was so grateful she cared enough to sew for me." She paused and looked at me. "People should show appreciation. I don't know why some people don't," she said strongly. "All it takes is a simple thank you."

"Thank you," I said.

"For what?"

"For everything."

"You want me to sew something for you, is that it?" She looked at me suspiciously.

"No. Well, maybe. You know that nightshirt you made for me a couple of months ago?"

"Yes, of course."

"I think I ripped it."

"You think?"

"Just a small rip."

"And you want me to sew it up?"

"I'd really appreciate it."

And I did.

33. Factory

I'm a factory," she said.

"What?" She didn't look like a factory. She was bent over the sewing machine finishing off a sash that went with the dress she had just completed for one of our granddaughters.

"I'm a sweatshop," she said.

"You don't look as if you're sweating," I said. She looked cool and calm and cute. She cut the last piece of thread and lifted the presser foot and turned off the machine.

"And I don't even get near minimum wage," she said.

"You're retired," I said, confused by all her comments.

"Hah!" she said. She let out the exclamation with a gust of air. "Let me tell you, I know what it's like to be a factory."

"This isn't a factory," I said, still puzzled. The sewing room looked normal, the same as it always did. Her thread was lined up in cones and spools on the shelves. Her fabric was stacked all over the room. Her notions filled cabinets and drawers and racks. Boxes of patterns were stacked against the walls.

"I'm a factory worker then. I should have my own sewers' union and fight for better working conditions."

"The house is air-conditioned. Your kitchen is down the hall full of food. You have big bright windows looking out over a lawn and trees. There are birds flying everywhere. You have two new machines. You are healthy and happy," I said.

"I need more freedom," she said.

"You are free."

"Hah!" She gave me *that* look and turned back to the dress. She fitted it to a hanger and hung it on the hook over the closet door. I watched her pat out a few creases, and then I thought I knew what she was talking about. Beneath that dress, in the same fabric, in the same size, was an identical dress. We have two granddaughters and, therefore, she had made two dresses. Beneath the dresses hung a shirt for our grandson, and a pair of overalls, size six months, for our grandson to be. The dresses, the shirt, and the overalls were all made of the same fabric. All four pieces were blue cotton and were covered by small airplanes being flown by wild animal creatures. All of them were darling. Our grandchildren would love them, I was sure.

"They're all very cute," I said, as she looked at them.

"Of course they're cute," she said. "Why wouldn't they be cute? If I made a hundred more, they would be as cute as these. But I don't want to do any more. It's not the same as when I just make one. But I can't just make one because then the other grandkids will want one and ask me why I didn't make them the same and I won't be able to explain it and then they'll all hate me and I'll have to give up sewing and I don't want to do that."

Well, that explained it. She was a factory, mass-producing children's clothing.

"It's your fault," she said then, throwing the words at me before I could say anything.

"My fault?"

"You made me buy all that material."

"It was the end of the bolt and it was on sale and what does that have to do with anything?" I said.

"If I only had fabric for one outfit, then I would have made something else for the others. You forced me to use all the material, so naturally I had to make all the grandkids something similar."

"I forced you?"

"Yes," she said. But she was smiling.

"I forced you to buy the sewing machine and the serger and all the fabric and the thread and the notions, and I forced you to sit in here the past three days sewing your little head off?"

"Of course," she said.

"Well, you don't have to ever sew again," I said. "I'll call up the thrift shops tomorrow and they can come over and we can give everything away." Hah!

"We can't."

"Oh, and why not?"

"I still have to make the baby clothes and the shorts and everything else I planned."

"And what about your being a factory?"

"I'm only going to make one of each."

"You're not a sweat shop either?"

"Not if you take me out to dinner and give me a raise."

"I don't pay you now. How could I give you a raise?"

"I could buy some new fabric. I saw some cute designs in the new catalog."

"I'm not a fabric store," I said, trying to make this conversation come out even.

"No, but I know where some are. Come on, I'll show you," she said, and she reached for my hand.

I followed. Somehow, I realized, I was married to a garment factory, a sweatshop, and someone who definitely should get paid the new minimum wage.

34. Zipper Code

The zipper is stuck," she said, her tone one of great frustration. Having as a child spent many hours fixing zippers for my parents in their tailor shop, I went to her rescue. As a child and as a young teenager, fixing zippers was a regular job for me. When a garment came into my parents' shop with a broken zipper or if one jammed while cleaning or pressing it, my father would give it to me to see if fixing it was possible. As it sometimes took a half hour or longer to fix the zipper, my father could not waste valuable time working on it. My time was not so valuable.

"Is it jammed?" I asked.

"No, the zipper's fine. I just can't figure out how to sew it into the jacket."

"Did you follow the pattern?" I asked. Sometimes she did. Sometimes she didn't.

"The pattern is another crazy pattern. The directions are impossible, and even if they were clear, they don't work. I tried it fifty-two different ways."

"Let me see," I said wisely. Knowing that if there wasn't anything wrong with the zipper, my zipper-fixing skills would not be called into play, and I couldn't be a hero and get many happy rewards, I tried to make her feel that at least I was trying to help. I looked at the pattern. I looked at what she had sewn. I read the directions. I rolled my eyes and stretched my arms and stomped my foot. Then I went, "Hmmmmm."

"Well?"

"The directions are impossible," I confirmed and gave her back the pattern. I didn't know if they were really impossible. I just think all directions in patterns are impossible. Why should these have been so different?

"I'm going to do it my way," she said, both defeated by the directions and inspired to rescue the jacket from doom.

"Do you need any more help?" I asked helpfully.

"No."

"All right," I said, and I went back to watch the news.

An hour later I heard her yell, "Yippee!" The sound rocked the house. I knew it was time to stop watching the news and go celebrate something with her. I hoped it was the zipper.

Her sewing room was a shambles. It was a jungle of clothes scattered all over. My first thought was that her gleeful cheer was to celebrate her having found her way free of the mess I saw. I looked more closely at the mess. There were sweatshirts and jackets and coats all over. It was a weekend flea market in her room. It was a hundred thrift shops all in one.

"I did it," she said.

"You made a mess," I said. I shoveled some clothes aside so I could get to her at her sewing machine. I looked at the clothes crumpled and piled all over. Then I saw that they all had one thing in common. It wasn't their color or fabric or whether they were winter clothes or summer clothes. No, they all had zippers.

"I needed some samples," she said.

"You certainly have enough samples," I said.

"I had to see how the zippers were put in," she said, very matter-of-factly.

"And were they put in correctly?" I asked.

"Of course. But I had to find one put in like the one in the jacket I'm making. I found one that was just right."

"Like Goldilocks?"

"What?"

"The Three Bears."

"Bears don't have zippers," she said. "The pattern directions *are* wrong. But I got the zipper in by looking at one that was done the right way."

"Is the jacket done?" I asked.

"No, I still have the hood."

"And what if the directions aren't clear?"

"I'm not using directions. Don't you think I've done hoods before?" She glared. "I've done hundreds of hoods, thousands."

"More than Little Red Riding Hood?" I asked, but she didn't answer that question.

"Couldn't you just clean up this room a little for me? You know I don't like to work in a messy room."

"Sure, Honey," I said, and I cleaned up the room. If a woman who sews needs a little help now and then, who am I to refuse?

35. Withdrawal

The first half hour of the drive home was quite all right. I kept up a steady patter of conversation to keep her mind off those last few terrible moments. Going back into the house was all right, too. I looked at her carefully. She seemed a little quiet, but I expected that. She started down the hall toward the back of the house, but I managed to steer her into the kitchen instead. "What about dinner now? I'll help," I said. Eating might distract her.

"No, not now. I'm not hungry." Her voice was even, without emotion. There was a slight chill in it.

"Something to drink?"

"I am a little warm. Some water will do."

I opened the refrigerator and took out the chilled water and poured her a glass. She stood still in the middle of the kitchen and didn't move. I gave her the glass. She sipped it and handed it back.

"I feel cold," she said.

"Some coffee, then?"

"All right." I began to make the coffee. "No, never mind. I think I'll go lie down for a while. I feel warm now. Clammy." She wiped at her brow.

"Maybe some yogurt?" A shake of her head. "A sandwich?" Another shake. She still hadn't moved from where she first stood.

"I'm sorry," she said. "I don't think anything will do any good. Maybe later. I'm going to lie down." She moved finally, away from me and out of the kitchen. I followed her down the hall toward the bedroom, my fingers crossed for luck, a silent prayer said with each step, but it was no use. She turned away from the bedroom into the sewing room. She snapped on the overhead light. The room took on an awful brightness. She stopped and looked at the backside of the room at the empty sewing table, that table now so bare.

"I shouldn't have done it," she said, her body trembling, her voice on edge, her face pale.

"It wasn't your fault. It needed service. We had to take it in."

"It's my first serger."

"It'll be ready in two days. I told them to hurry." She looked at me, lost and forlorn.

"I need the serger back. Call them. Tell them I don't care if it needs servicing. It should never need servicing. I want it back. I need it back. Look at me...."

"You look wonderful," I began, but her looked stopped me. "It's only withdrawal, Hon. You'll get over it. I'll stay with you. We'll lick this thing together. I'll be right here."

"Promise?" she said.

"Promise," I answered. I looked at the clock: forty-seven hours to go.

36. Cutting

But you promised two days," I argued into the mouthpiece.
I needed no urgency to express my anger. My wife had
already waited a painful two days for her serger to be returned. When
we had not heard from the service people after two days, I called,
only to receive the message that the store was closed for the weekend.
It would be Monday morning before the serger was ready.

"The repair man had to take his wife to the hospital Saturday," was
the calm reply from the store owner. "But it's ready now."

"It's ready now?" I asked, apology already in my voice.

"Sorry for the delay," he said. He was used to dealing with us, them,
the husbands and wives who had brought in sewing machines and
sergers wanting them the day before yesterday.

"Thanks. We'll be right out." Even if it meant going on our lunch
hour and skipping a meal we could easily do without, we were on our
way. My urgency to drive across town was by now, after seventy-two
hours, as strong as my wife's. She just wanted her machine back. I
wanted my whole life back.

Everything really had been fine for the first twenty-four hours. I
walked her around the block. I took her out to dinner. She went to
her gym three times, hoping to exhaust herself and calm herself
down. I cuddled her, hugged her, gave her my all, and we thought
she had the situation licked. But as it came closer to the deadline,
those original forty-eight hours almost over, no call came to tell us
the serger was ready. All my good deeds, all my comfort, seemed to
no avail. The Red Cross, the Salvation Army, disaster agencies—none
could have helped. So that was why I finally called the store and got
that fateful message that the store was closed until Monday. I knew
what every defeated general must have known throughout history—

that so-often-spoken agony of defeat. But I had to tell her. There was no one else to tell her.

She listened to me tell her. I didn't mince words. "The place is closed. It'll be Monday." I readied myself for her sorrowful cry in response. But none came. I waited for the bellow of pain, but there was only more silence.

She looked down at the floor for a moment and then lifted her head and faced me directly. "No problem," she said. No problem? I began to panic inside. My stomach churned. The whole world was topsy-turvy and she calmly says, "No problem."

"Honey, if I can do anything—" I tried again. She didn't answer. She turned from me and walked slowly down the hall to her sewing room. Dare I follow? I quickly recalled our years together, that flashback full of every similar situation we had ever been in. None matched. But I knew not to follow her. Give her some space, I told myself. I followed my advice and left her alone.

I didn't really see her for the next twelve hours. I heard her. Yes, I heard some clinking and some clanking and an occasional snipping and snapping, but I kept my distance. I went through my day, downloaded some new shareware from the Net, collected her sewing mail, and generally passed the time away. But still, through it all, through lunch and dinner when I sat alone at the table, I wondered how she was managing.

"I'm going to bed," I said finally, raising my voice for her to hear through the closed door of her sewing room. There was no reply, but I heard paper rustling and cutting and an occasional mild exclamation of frustration. I left her alone. I would give her until morning.

And morning certainly came. I rose and showered and dressed and went to her door and knocked gently. No answer. I knocked again, waited, and still no answer. I began to worry. I turned the knob to open the door, but the door remained in place. I pushed. It moved slightly. It wasn't locked, but there was something pushing back against me. I had visions of her collapsed in a heap on the floor, these last hours overcoming her like some poisonous vapor from some witch's curse. I pushed against some heavy mysterious force and finally opened the door enough to squeeze myself into the room.

She lay asleep on a pile of fabric. Around her, spread across the cutting table, spread on the floor, spread up against all the walls, were piles and piles of fabric, all in neat piles, all cut to various shapes. "Honey, are you all right?" I shook her, but I suspected now she lay only in exhaustion.

"I used all my patterns," she muttered, but the words were crisp, matter-of-fact. I looked around some more. I saw that each piece of fabric wasn't some remnant scattered wildly around the room. Each piece of fabric had a section of pattern pinned to it. She saw my head turn and she heard me gasp in my wonderment. "I'm ready to sew now," she said, a tiny but firm smile curling her lips. And as if to explain to this dunderhead who might not understand how she got through the third day of her waiting, she added, "I cut out every pattern I have. All the size twos and threes and fours." She paused, shook herself, stood boldly and grabbed my hand to drag me after her. "I'm ready to sew now. Let's go get the serger. And on the way home, let's stop at the fabric store to see if they have any new patterns for cute things in sizes five and six."

"Absolutely," I said, relieved and ecstatic. Oh, yes, absolutely.

37. Honey, Be a Dear...

I need more room," she said.

"More room for what?" I asked. I had heard this request so many times before.

"For my patterns."

"You already have plenty of room for your patterns," I said. She had plenty of room.

"I just cut out some new ones," she said. "My pattern boxes are full."

"Why don't you put away the old ones in the garage?" I asked. "The grandkids have outgrown all those sizes." Now what is wrong with that sensible idea?

"There will be a new grandkid. There may be others. I need them."

"They'll still be close by."

"Not close enough."

"How close do they have to be?"

"Right next to my cutting table."

"Right next to the *new* cutting table?" She had taken over another table in what used to be her office. Now that she was retired, the office had become a pantry. Now the pantry was also a cutting room. Why did I think our house was getting smaller and smaller?

"Bring back the old filing cabinet," she said. "Then I can file all the patterns."

"That's a lot of work," I said. "The filing cabinet's big and heavy. Why can't you just put them in the filing cabinet where it is?" The old filing cabinet was in the garage and the garage was only thirty feet from the pantry/cutting room. "It's not far to go."

"It's hot and dusty in the garage in the summer, and it's cold and dusty in the winter."

"All right." I'm easy. "When do you want to do it?" Never ask a sewer when she wants to get anything ready that has to do with sewing.

"Right now."

"During breakfast?"

"After breakfast is all right."

"What about all the free space you'll have when you move the patterns out of your sewing room?" I chewed my food very slowly.

"It's reserved."

"It's reserved? For what?" I never really need to ask these questions.

"I ordered some more fabric and notions and patterns."

"More patterns?"

"The grandkids are getting bigger. I have to keep ahead."

"How many years in advance?" The oldest was five, the youngest was going to turn three.

"Up to size twelve. Up to small, medium, and large."

"That's at least five or six years from now," I said, logic my strong point.

"They grow fast," she said. What does logic have to do with sewing?

So, I finished my breakfast and drank the last of my decaffeinated coffee, though I should have gone with the caffeine. I went out to the garage and, with a lot of groaning and grunting, I moved the filing cabinet. I dragged it into the house and put it next to the cutting table. "Is that it?" I asked when I was done, when my back ached and I was exhausted.

"For now," she said. But she had *that* look on her face. I think she was wondering if that one filing cabinet would be enough.

38. Head's Up

She was wandering from room to room, every few minutes letting out a tiny squeal. "Oylp," or "Elp," or "Ipil."

"Now what?" I asked.

"I'm sorry," she said.

"Sorry for what?" I asked. I knew what she was sorry for. She was sorry for my head. I had just had a hair transplant. I belonged to my own personal hair club, but the addition to my head was not enough to be noticeable except by anyone looking at my head. And they would always ask, "What happened to your head?"

"Sewing," I answered. Of course that answer would puzzle them and they'd look at me for an explanation, and after a while I got tired of giving explanations, so now I am writing it down once and for all.

I didn't get a hair transplant. I am not vain. And if I had had any reason to add hair to my head, it wouldn't have been such a tiny amount. Four strands of hair, and they would last only about ten days.

Ah, so what does this have to do with sewing? Everything and nothing.

It began when for the four-hundredth time over the past year she came out of her sewing room with a disgusted look on her face. I knew that look. It was a look that was saying, "I can't stand the sewing room any more. We have to paint it."

"We don't have to paint it," I said. If she ever became serious about it, I would hire a painter.

"This time, I'm serious," she said.

"Absolutely serious?" I asked. She had been serious before, but never absolutely serious. After all, this was her sewing room she was talking about. Every time we talked about getting it painted, she realized she would have to take everything out of the room. It had taken a year to get every piece of sewing paraphernalia into the room, the serger, the sewing machine, the hundred or more spools of thread (fifty of serger thread alone), the yards and yards of fabric, the notions, the sewing books, the boxes of patterns, the rolls of patterns, the half-finished projects, the finished projects, and everything else that filled every nook and cranny from wall to wall and floor to ceiling. I always believed she would never have the patience, the time, the courage, to empty out her room. But this time she was serious.

"Call the painter," she said.

"Call the painter?" I asked, incredulous. It had never gotten this far before.

"Call him," she said, and after thirty-six years of marriage I knew her tone of voice meant, "Call the painter."

Emptying the room took a week. It was on the third day when I was bending, actually crawling on the floor, to pull out lamp cords and sewing machine cords and extension cords and ironing cords, when it happened. And of course it was dumb and stupid and careless and idiotic that I stood up right under a shelf and cracked my head on the edge of a fluorescent lamp. It was dumber still that the edge of the lamp was made of sheet metal and had a very sharp edge.

"Don't bleed on any of the fabric," I expected her to say, but of course she didn't. She ran to get me a clean bandage and some alcohol and helped to clean the wound.

"Is it deep?" I asked, my head throbbing something like her serger sometimes does when the needle is bent and hits against the upper looper.

"I can't tell," she said.

"Well, we'll finish here later, if that's all right, and we can go to the emergency room and see if I need stitches." We could finish empty-ing that room years later for all I cared at that moment.

And so, off we went.

Now, this doesn't sound much like a sewing story, but really, it is. For after the nurse cleaned the wound and called in the doctor, he told me that it was deeper than it looked. It was my hair loss that made it easy for the doctor to find the wound and tell me, "A couple of stitches will do it."

"What kind of stitches?" my wife asked, for she was in the room, sitting quietly, still in some kind of shock at my injury.

"What?" asked the doctor.

"You said stitches. What kind? And what kind of needle are you going to use?"

Now, this was a nice doctor, a doctor who had before him an injured man, a doctor who had a waiting room full of other injured patients waiting to be patched up. So he was patient. He didn't know my wife knew her sewing. "Just a couple of small stitches," he said.

"Topstitch?" my wife asked.

"Yes, of course, on the top," said the doctor. He was already injecting pain killer into my scalp.

"An embroidery stitch?" she asked. "Use a hoop. You could make him look nice."

The doctor chuckled.

"How about an invisible stitch," she suggested. The nurse began to giggle, as she handed the doctor the suture.

"Or a nice satin stitch would look good," she said, changing her mind.

"She really wants you to use a three-thread overlock with a rolled edge," I said. Why not? He must have already been confused. He entered the first stitch.

"It looks like you'll need a couple more," the doctor said. "It's a wider cut than I thought."

When, a moment later, he finished, she stood and looked at my head. "Hand sewing is a fine art," she said to the doctor. "You can come home and sew with me anytime." The highest compliment.

"Can I go now?" I asked. I had enough sewing for one day.

"Of course," the doctor said. "Come back in eight days and I'll take the stitches out."

"Couldn't I do that?" my Darling Wife asked, and before the doctor could understand what she was asking, before she told him she had a seam ripper at home that might do a lovely job of removing the stitches on my head, I climbed down from the table, grabbed my wife's hand, and hurried her out of there.

"Thanks, Doctor," I said behind me.

"Yes, thank you," my wife said to everyone in the emergency room. Then she turned to me and said, "He has a good technique. Maybe he can join our sewing list and give us some tips."

"I'll ask him next week," I said.

AUGUST

39. Return Policy

*T*he hood is just a little tight. When he puts it on, the jacket rides up and squishes his neck. He makes strange choking sounds."

"It could be a little larger," my wife said.

"And the buttons in front of the bib of her overalls are too close together, so the front billows out."

"The buttons can be moved," my wife said.

"And the waist on the shorts is loose and the shorts slide down to his knees when he climbs a tree."

"So, shorten the elastic and take in the waist." My Darling Wife has the ideal return policy. No thirty days or sixty days or one year or two. Her products are guaranteed forever. By the time she delivers the clothes to the grandchildren and she hears, "Thank you," along with the squealing of joy, she has already known the pleasure of deciding the design of the outfit, selecting the fabric, cutting the pattern to a workable size, and sewing the garment. She is overwhelmed with the happiness of having sewed something new and bright for the grand-children. Giving the clothes to them is the final joy. And usually that is it, until the next time.

But because the children all live far away, fitting them as she sews is impossible, so she has to have a return policy.

"Let them try it on. Then I'll know for next time." Never mind that next time the kids may be a foot or two taller. (Don't they grow that much in three weeks?) Or they may have torn out a seam or two. (God forbid, it happens.) Or they may complain that they can't swallow their peanut butter and jelly sandwiches because the turtle-neck collar or ribbing is too tight. (Let them drink milk.)

The policy is not a tough one for the children, for when they like something, they like it. Just try to take away the pajamas for a few days to send back to Grandma to shorten the waist or lengthen the legs. It would be untold pain accompanied by tears, tantrums, and hunger strikes. Better to sell them into slavery than to deny them their "special" clothes. Rest assured, the children will wear them just the way they are.

But it happens. Every great once in a while, the clothes do not fit perfectly. If and when that happens, the project becomes practice for the next one.

"He seems to be growing more in the torso, so when you make the next one, would you enlarge the chest?" At five, he has been working out too much, no doubt.

"She likes the hem to be at her knees, so could you make the next one three inches longer?" (She is almost four and certainly cannot go to preschool with the wrong hemline.)

"She's tired of purple and wants something in gold with small flowers, but not daisies."

"He still likes dinosaurs, but he's getting interested in sports. Do they have fabric with basketballs?" (He is five and already looks forward to playing in the NBA.)

So my wife has a liberal return policy. But it, like most warranties today, is limited. The small print reads: "No repairs, alterations, resizing, tailoring, dyeing, additions, or otherwise changing anything from its original design, fabric, shape, or color. All the former will be done by the children's own mothers. I will accept, and maybe take into account, brief comments regarding changes in the children's growth patterns, either up, out, or in, but only for future reference. All sales are final." Signed, "Grandma."

40. Babyland

We went to the local Country Arts Fair last Sunday. Darling Wife stopped at every booth and checked over everything that at one time resembled fabric and now was a garment of some kind. "There are billions of neat things here," she said.

"Neat things?" I asked, trying to hurry her along. If I let her linger too long, I might never get home to have lunch or dinner or breakfast the next morning. We had been to hundreds of these fairs in the past years and I know her. But it was even worse now that she was sewing every day and needed some fresh ideas.

"Wonderful things," she added, and I could see her mind taking mental pictures of everything, as she always did when she saw something she might sew herself some day.

I, too, was amazed at the variety of clothing and the quantity of it. In one booth it looked as if someone had bought two hundred plain denim dresses and painted every one of them into a spectacle of color. "I don't do paint," my wife said, quickly passing them by.

We moved slowly from booth to booth, stopping now and then as she went berserk at what she saw, but I calmed her after each foray and we moved on. Then we saw the booth with baby clothes.

Now, a week before, we added a grandson to our growing family, the second grandson to match in number the two granddaughters. The baby was now a week old. My sweet, caring, sewing-headed wife had already sewn infant shirts and pajamas and baby bunting, but she was aching to make something else.

"Look, Honey," she shouted.

"Yes, Dear," I said patiently, as she pointed a wild arm, hand, and finger at a group of gaily decorated bibs hanging in front of a booth.

Now, I have heard this lady make all kinds of sounds when she had a new idea for sewing, but nothing before had matched this combination coo, exclamation, yell, gasp, and quiet scream that came out of her mouth. Her whole face curled into a smile of delight. Encouraged by her reaction to a few baby bibs, I moved closer to see them and touch them, and I did feel some of the pleasure of their quality. I was impressed.

"I'm going to make bibs like these," she said. That was it. No more. She stared at the bibs, gulped a few times, rolled her eyes a bit, and finally she sighed. "Let's go," she said.

"We haven't seen everything," I protested, but it was a weak protest, just for show.

"Let's go," she said. "I have to make bibs."

It is now three days later. My exhausted wife is eating breakfast, each bite the struggle of a woman who hasn't eaten enough the past three days. Each yawn between bites the gasping for breath of a woman who hasn't slept enough the past few nights. But in her room, gift wrapped in small bundles, are about a billion bibs.

She had only intended to make one bib, following the pattern she had copied in her mind from those she saw at the crafts fair. Two-sided, rickrack trim, loops for teething rings, Velcro fasteners. "How do you like it?" she asked, as she showed me the finished project.

"It's great," I said, and it was. She had made the bib, attached an appliqué, embroidered our new grandson's name on it, and it was lovely.

"I'm going to make some more," she said. "One's never enough."

"Yes, kids drool a lot," I said. She just looked at me. The look told me I was in the way.

Like Rumpelstiltskin spinning gold out of straw, she went into a fury of bib-making. All the scraps in her stash of scraps that were large enough, she used to make a bib. One-two-three-four-five. No two were alike. Whatever had been the original pattern was long gone. Six-seven-eight-nine-ten.

"Isn't that enough?" I asked after she showed me each one.

"No." Eleven-twelve-thirteen.

It was only when I dragged her outside for a breath of fresh air that she stopped production, but just in case, she had left the serger and sewing machine on. Outside, I thought she would smell the fresh air, the first after Santa Ana winds had blown dust into our sky one hundred fifty miles away from where the same winds pushed fires across Southern California. But outside, we ran into a neighbor whose daughter-in-law had just given birth to a baby girl. Uh, oh!

Fourteen-fifteen-sixteen. And what about the couple down the street who had a six-month-old boy? Our friends across town who had a three-month-old girl? Seventeen-eighteen-nineteen-twenty. Help!

Well, she is eating now, and the sewing machine is off, and she seems better now.

"You know what?" she said.

"What?" Maybe she wanted to take a nap.

"I think I'll make just a few more."

"There's no one left in the world that doesn't have a bib," I said. I was probably correct about that, but if she was thinking of going down to the maternity rooms of our local hospitals to see....

"No, I think I'll make a few for you."

"For me? I don't need a bib."

"For when you get old."

"Why when I get old?"

"For when you are old and you begin to drool," she said. "Yes, just a few more."

41. Pockets

Ahhh-choo," she sneezed.

"Bless you."

"I need a Kleenex," she said.

"I don't have any."

"What should I do?"

"Don't sneeze."

"You men."

"What does that mean?"

"You have all those pockets and you don't have a Kleenex."

"Why don't you have pockets? Then you could carry everything you wanted. Kleenex, fabric, needles, your serger. Whatever you wanted."

I expected her to break one or two of my bones, but instead she stood quietly and took a moment to look at me. Then, she spoke. "Good idea," she said.

And so began her new project. She called it her "Pocket Project." I called it her "Lost Weekend." No, she didn't drown herself in alcohol. She disappeared into the world of her sewing room on Friday afternoon, and I think I saw her wandering around the kitchen Monday morning. In between ... well ... she made pockets.

"I even made some welt pockets," she said after dragging me into her sewing room. She dangled a flowered cotton dress in front of me. Sure enough, there were two tailored pockets sewn into the front of the dress. She held the dress out to me and I put my hands in the pockets. She had filled the pockets with several pieces of Kleenex.

"Now, you're set," I said.

"That's not all," she said. "I went through all my closets."

"All your closets?" Now that was something. Not only did she have the closets in her sewing room and the bedroom and the hall, she also had all my closets. She owned the closets in the house. I was lucky to have room for a shirt and a pair of pants, a small shirt and a small pair of pants.

"Even the wardrobes in the garage," she answered.

"And what did you find?" I asked. Why not ask?

"I found a lot of dresses without pockets."

"A lot of dresses?" I always had to question her use of "a few" or "a lot" or "some."

"All my fall dresses and winter dresses and spring dresses."

"That's a lot of dresses," I said. "And you found some without pockets?"

"You don't know how many. I think when I was in junior high school sewing class we were told not to have pockets. We were told that instead we should have men with pockets."

"You learned that in sewing class?"

"Home Economics. It included tips for dating and marriage."

"But no tips on pockets?"

"No, but I have pockets now."

"In all your dresses?"

"Lots of dresses. I'm not done yet. Look." She brought forward another dress from a hook jutting out over a closet door. The small hook held about ninety-nine dresses. The dress had deep pockets sewn into the side seam.

"You made different kinds of pockets?"

"All kinds of pockets." She was setting me up again.

"What kinds of pockets?" As a sweet, caring, darling husband, I had to ask.

Stories by Popser

"Bound pockets, patch-lined, regular-lined, unlined, sport pockets, side pockets, pockets with flaps and pockets without flaps, round pockets and square pockets." She stopped and caught her breath. "Some are very hard to sew, you know."

"Not for you," I said.

"Do you want me to show them all to you?"

"Do I have a choice?"

"No."

So I saw them all, and as I looked at her work, her craftwomanship, I put my hands into all the pockets. Every pocket of every kind in every dress had Kleenex in it.

"Ah-choo," I said to her. "Do you have a Kleenex?"

"Get your own," she said.

42. Call to Action

It began last winter in the kitchen when I accidentally splashed a few drops of bleach off the countertop I was cleaning onto my new sweatshirt. "Yuck!" I said to myself. But Darling Wife about a half a mile away in her sewing room heard me and came running.

"What is it?" she asked, looking all over to see what I might have done, what casserole I might have dropped on the floor, or what ghastly mess I might have encountered in the back of the refrigerator, which she kept spotless.

"No problem," I said. "I was just cleaning the grout on the tile," I said.

"Oh," she said, relieved there was no major catastrophe to interrupt her sewing day. She ran the distance to the back of the house and back to her sewing in three seconds flat.

I, on the other hand, removed my plum colored sweatshirt and put it into the hamper. When it was washed the next day, the white bleach stains dotted the front of the shirt. I grabbed the shirt before she could see it and put it with the "cleaning house, yard, and neighborhood clothes bin" in the garage.

Last weekend it turned unseasonably windy and cold and rainy. When the quick storm was over, I prepared to go clean the leaves and pine cones and other mess the rain had left on the front yard. It was chilly enough for a working man's sweatshirt, stains or no stains. When I put it on, she saw the bleach stains and gave me her "Well, when did that happen?" look.

"Last year," I said before she spoke.

"It's an eyesore," she said.

"Just a few stains. It's perfect for yard work," I said.

"No, you can't go out wearing that. Let me do something with it."

Now, "Let me do something with it" is my wife's clarion cry and my warning to run and hide. It was the ultimate signal that my shirt was going to be revamped, remodeled, restructured, changed, converted. I knew the shrill cry of some medieval sewer's trumpet and I knew it was best not to resist whatever actions her sewing-mind was planning.

"Birds or flowers or fish or cars or something else?" she asked.

"Something else," I answered, not knowing at all what she was asking, but "something else" gave me some choice.

"All right," she said with no further explanation. I didn't question her.

I got another shirt and went out and raked and scooped and dumped leaves and pine cones and enjoyed the crisp air. When I went back into the house, she greeted me with an exultant cry of, "Here you go." She held my sweatshirt in front of her.

I looked at it. What had before been a sweatshirt spotted with bleach stains was now a sweatshirt covered with small appliqués. Across the front of the shirt, strategically placed, were yellow and red leaves falling down from some invisible tree. Each leaf, delicately cut, hid the stains forever.

"How's that, Mr. Stain-your-shirt-and-hide-it-from-me-for-a-year Husband?"

"It's beautiful," I said.

"So now you'll be able to wear it in the neighborhood without shame?"

"Absolutely," I said. Oh, yes, without doubt.

"And you'll be proud, as you go out into the world?"

"Proud," I said.

"So, do you have any other messes you've made of your clothes? I can put appliqués on anything, you know."

"Well, I do have that pair of cords I burned when I backed into the barbecue last summer," I said without thinking. The burn was not on the legs, not on the waist, not on the front, not anywhere but where I was really sure I didn't want an appliqué.

"Oh, go get them. I have some nice pink butterflies left over from a skirt I made. They'll be just the thing."

"Butterflies?" I asked. I was thinking more in the line of invisible mending.

"Go get the pants," she said pleasantly.

I knew enough to get the pants, and she patched the pants with pink butterflies, and they are beautiful. They're stored now somewhere in the garage where I can find them some time in the future if I ever have to do yard work on a dark night. Very dark and very late at night. As for the sweatshirt, I wear it all the time. I think it looks neat.

43. Valance

"*V*alance: A short drapery, decorative board, or metal strip mounted especially across the top of a window to conceal structural fixtures." (American Heritage Dictionary)

After I bought and installed the curtain rod in her sewing room, she began a search for the perfect fabric for the valance. The new pleated shade was a hue of rose, and she wanted something to match it and the newly painted Atrium-white wall. Though the color of the shade was called Serenity Horizon, she thought the color of the shade was a dusty rose, and I thought it was more a puce rose. In any case, she rummaged through the fifteen or so tons of fabric in her stash and found a lightweight piece of fabric covered with rose-colored roses that, miraculously, matched. In her eagerness to begin her project, she broke the first size-seventy needle she put in her serger, but she soon gained control of herself, took a deep breath, and produced a valance that she hung neatly on the rod. Then she called me in to see her work.

"It looks great," I said, actually astonished that it looked so good. I wasn't astonished by her work; rather, I was astonished that I had been wrong when I had said, "Your room doesn't need a valance." She was right. Though we both thought the room looked great before, the room now looked better by far. So she was pleased. And I thought that was the end of it.

I was wrong.

"Hear that?" she asked me the other morning. I was sitting at the kitchen table reading an article about the wise use of leisure time. As all my time now was leisure time, or so I believed, the article did not inspire me. I was glad of her interruption.

"Hear what?" I asked. I rarely heard anything when I was reading. She didn't understand this. I could read with the television going, the wind howling, the dishwasher grinding away, and not hear a thing. She could hear a needle being threaded in China.

"The window," she said.

"Was there an earthquake?" I asked. The window often made creaking sounds when the temperature outside changed dramatically. The window made sounds when the house settled. But I heard nothing.

"No, not that kind of sound."

"What kind then?" I asked. I always had to ask.

"It's naked," she said.

"What's naked?" I asked. I was calm.

"The window's naked."

"It looks all right to me," I said. I regarded the window carefully. The mini-blinds were down and closed so the morning sun just barely filtered through. No lewdness there.

"It feels undressed," she said. I stared at the window a moment and then turned to her with my standard puzzled look.

"And?" I asked gingerly.

"And it wants a valance," she said. Aha!

"It told you that?" I asked seriously. I knew what was coming.

"It knows the sewing room window has a valance. It wants one, too."

"It's envious?"

"This house has been together a long time," she said. "Each room knows what's going on in the other rooms. This room wants a valance."

"I didn't hear it say that."

"You never listen. Now, are you going to buy another curtain rod?"

"No."

"But you know how good it would look to have a valance over the window."

"It would never end. I know you. First this window, then the bathroom window, then the living room window, then the bedroom, and then the study. My study doesn't want a valance. My desk and filing cabinet and computer and, yes, the window, are all quite happy the way they are and don't want a valance. Once you begin down that slippery slope in the kitchen...."

"I'll go see," she said, interrupting. "I hadn't thought about the study. I think I have just the right fabric for that room."

"There is no right fabric," I insisted. I had to head her off.

"Well, you're right. That can wait until I finish in here. Then we'll let the room decide."

"Rooms don't decide anything," I said, wanting to put an end to talking windows and talking rooms. I know she talked to her sewing machines, but that was it. No more.

"You can help me pick out the fabric," she said then, oh, so sweetly.

"No." I was firm.

"It will make this room look happy," she tried.

"I don't want a happy room."

"It will make me happy," she cooed.

"Maybe next year," I said, weakening, but I wouldn't surrender.

"Promise?" she asked.

"All right," I promised.

"Good. I have plenty to do this month. Then in September, I can make the valance."

"I didn't mean September." I hadn't thought about next month. I had thought only of never.

"I heard you promise. This house heard you promise. Did we hear wrong?"

"No, *you* didn't hear wrong." I stopped while she was ahead. If I bought her some more pattern books and the grandkids kept growing out of their old clothes, maybe it would be the next century before she would get around to the kitchen window. Maybe, just maybe, she'd forget about it. Want to bet on it?

September

43. White on White

I should never have answered her when, after she did her monthly inventory of The Stash, she discovered about six yards of white cotton fabric.

"I remember this. I was going to make some pinafores," she said.

"You still can." She would have to put it on her project calendar for the year two thousand thirty. That's how many projects she was already working on.

"No, I think I remember that this fabric wouldn't be right. I need to think of something else," she said, musing.

"Well, there's no hurry," I said helpfully.

"What do you think?" she asked then, her question surprising me.

"You want my opinion?" I asked, bewildered that she would. I looked at the fabric. "I haven't the slightest idea," I said.

"Oh, you can think of something," she insisted.

"Sheets," I said. Maybe I was taking some association test.

"No, we have plenty of sheets and, besides, when winter comes, we'll use the flannel sheets I made last year. What else?"

I looked at the white fabric. Think white, I told myself. "Casper costumes for the grandkids. Halloween will be here in another month."

"No," she said. She had her finger to her forehead, as if she were thinking how limited my advice was. "They would never want to be ghosts. That's too easy."

"How about a white shirt?" I said.

"You don't wear white shirts any more. All you wear are all those old sweatshirts."

"Some are new," I replied. At least two were less than two years old.

"Think," she admonished.

"Handkerchiefs," I said. Actually, that was a good idea, I thought. I always use handkerchiefs. Come spring and hay fever, I would need a dozen.

"How many do you have now?" she asked in a very practical manner.

"A few," I answered.

"How many?" she asked again.

"Two or three dozen," I said. So, I didn't need handkerchiefs.

"You don't need any handkerchiefs," she said.

"A cook's hat?"

She shook her head.

"White neckties?"

"No."

"White boxer shorts?" A really long time ago I wore them.

"You know you won't wear them." I wouldn't. I began to squirm.

"Napkins," I said. I was grasping for any idea to save my neck before she strung me up as useless.

"Napkins," she said quietly to herself, as if what I had said was something to be seriously considered.

"They'd get dirty too fast," I said, trying to recover quickly and take the idea back. "White napkins and all that mustard and ketchup all over. Lipstick and cherry jam. Brown gravy or pomegranate juice."

"I have some black woolly nylon," she said, paying me absolutely no attention now. Was she even talking to me?

"What?" I asked.

"Rolled edge," she said.

"Huh?"

"Black and white," she said. And before I could raise an inquisitive eyebrow, she was gone. How she sometimes moved so quickly from my presence into her other world, in this case her sewing room, I never could understand. But I knew something I had just said had sent her off over the horizon.

It is all my fault. I take full responsibility. When, several hours later, I saw her again, she showed me her work. We now have two new white tablecloths and two dozen white napkins. Every piece of our new "tableware" is edged in black woolly nylon. I didn't have a moment to envision spaghetti sauce or blueberry preserves or maple syrup spilled on those tablecloths or wiped onto those napkins. She spoke too quickly.

"Now the woolly nylon feels useful," she said. "It was just waiting. Don't you think it's happy now?" she asked.

"Cotton and nylon," I said. "A marriage made in heaven. They should live happily ever after." She paid no attention to my attempt at humor.

"Oh, you should be happy, proud. It was your idea you know."

"It was a good idea, wasn't it?"

"Now what about that black corduroy I found in the back of the drawer. I think I have about three yards of it. Any ideas?"

"Sheets?" I offered.

"Oh, now you're being silly. I'll have to think of something," she said. And no doubt, she will.

44. Tale of the
South Pacific

*I*t was a Hawaiian day, warm and balmy, the trade breezes caressing our bodies in joyful pleasure. She was so taken by the paradise we were in that she didn't once mention sewing or fabric. The closest she came was to stare a moment into a store window at a Hawaiian dress. Seven days had gone by so far and not a word. No doubt she thought about it, but she was keeping her promise. It was to be a time of complete relaxation.

But the next day we changed islands, from Oahu to Kauai, and once installed in our new rental condo in the town of Kapaa, she wanted to go for a walk. We had walked the mornings, the afternoons, the early evenings, and walking had brought us few surprises, just sunshine and tired feet. But this "short" walk only a few short blocks from our resort brought us to the storefront of Vicky's. Vicky's is a fabric store. And the window showed Hawaiian prints and a pattern for a Hawaiian dress, sizes two through twelve. No doubt at that moment this Darling Grandmother heard the plaintive cries of our granddaughters three thousand miles away. "I think they want Hawaiian dresses," she said. "Muumuus," she added.

"What?" I heard her. I always heard her. Still dormant after a week of quiet, the volcano was rumbling.

"They really do need Hawaiian dresses," she began, her eyes fixed on a splash of flowered red and white fabric. "And the boys will need shirts," she said. One of the boys was five, but the other was three months old. I was certain he did not need any shirts at all.

"And you want to go inside?" I asked. I always asked. It was like some TV quiz game where I already knew the answer and had to ask the question.

"Just for a moment," she said. It was only moments before the eruption.

Five yards of this fabric and three yards of that fabric later, we were again out on the sidewalk.

"I'm sorry," she said.

"I understand," I said, grateful that she had not bought more. We had come with a minimum of luggage and had no space for anything more to take home.

Back at the condo she put the fabric in the small carry-on bag she had brought along, conveniently not yet full. Now it was full. No more room. Hah!

We managed two more days of island life, walking the beaches, meeting friends who lived on the island, sightseeing, enjoying the continued nice weather and thinking of all the people we knew who lived in the frigid or flooded parts of the mainland. Then our friends who lived on the island took us out for dinner.

"That's our new shopping area," our friends pointed out to us, as we drove the highway through the town of Kapaia toward the town of Lihue.

"We've done our shopping," I said. My Darling Wife nodded her head. No disagreement from her.

"Oh, look, there's the Kapaia Stitchery," our friends said in unison.

I didn't want to look. I didn't want anyone to look. "It's a nice day again," I said, hoping to distract them all.

"They have beautiful fabric," I heard from our friends in some Hawaiian chant.

"We already bought some fabric in Kapaa," my Darling Wife said. I hugged her for that. The volcano was inactive.

"Do you think it might rain tomorrow?" I asked, as we drove out of sight of the shop.

"We promised you good weather," we heard, and the promise was kept.

The next morning was so beautiful that we decided to take one more drive through the town and into the fields of sugar cane toward the lush green mountains. And it was then that this Napoleon met his Waterloo. I made a wrong turn and we were back on the highway going toward the town of Lihue again. Before we could reach the next intersection and turn the car around, she let out a small yelp.

"Stop," she said. I brought the car to a sudden halt along the road. Morning traffic yelled at us.

"Are you all right?" I asked.

"I'm sorry," she said.

"What's wrong?"

She lifted her hand and pointed across the road. I saw the sign boldly lit by sunshine. "Kapaia Stitchery."

"You want to go in?"

"I have to go in," she said. "I may never have the chance again."

"You said you wanted to come back here next year."

"In sewing time, that's forever," she said solemnly. She looked at me, her eyes begging.

I should have said no, for her own sake. She had promised. She had already given in once to the terrible temptation of Vicky's storefront window. I had to provide tough love and tell her no. "No," I said softly.

But it was too late. Her body was rigid, her eyes stared, her breathing became heavy. "Park over there," she said, pointing to a small parking lot in front of the shop. I looked at her, shook my head, and, as usual, gave in. I turned to park the car and we went inside.

I tried to drag her away from the bolt of red silk covered with white plumeria. I tried to push her past the bolts of green and brown tropical prints. But I was too weak from days in the sun, too exhausted from walking the beaches and splashing in the South Pacific. I had no will left to combat her need to shop. She bought five yards of Hawaiian fabric covered in ancient petroglyphs. Six yards of blue fabric covered in yellow and red hibiscus. I soon lost track. I ran outside to the car and held my breath until she came out. She got into the car. I didn't look at the packages. I drove us quickly away from there.

"Stop," she said.

Oh, no, not again! "What now?" I asked.

"There's a Wal-Mart."

"What do we need at Wal-Mart?" I asked. She would have an answer. No doubt about that.

"We need to get another carry-on," she said.

"What?" I was too confused already by the past hour with her.

"To carry home the fabric," she said. "You said we didn't have any room in our other bags, didn't you?"

"Yes, of course. I did say that. You're absolutely right. We do need another bag. Yes, oh, yes, we do. Why don't we get one now?"

And so we did.

45. All Wrong

I've never heard a banshee wail, but I suppose it sounds something like the sound I heard from her sewing room, and I am sure there is no Gaelic spirit in our house. Now, I know most of the sounds she makes when she is sewing, so I was surprised to hear this new one. I assumed, from its volume and length, it was serious. I jumped up from my chair in the living room, which at my age took a few minutes, and hurried down the hall to see what the problem was.

She was standing by the sewing machine with her back toward me. That was her normal position in that room, as she liked to sew facing the window so she would have just the perfect light when she was sewing.

"Are you all right?" I asked.

"It's all wrong," she said turning toward me. She wore the shirt she had been working on for the past two days. It was made out of the fabric she had bought in Hawaii and she looked pleasantly like a Hawaiian native. Flowers covered her from her hips to her neck.

"Nothing's all wrong," I said pleasantly. She didn't seem to be in pain, but she did have her lips turned down and her eyes seemed sadly dark. "Miss a buttonhole?" I asked. "Forget a few stitches? Have one sleeve longer than the other?" All these problems she could and would fix.

"No, everything's all wrong," she said. "Everything."

"The color? The style?"

"No, they're all right. But everything else."

"Show me," I said. She moved closer to me. I inspected her and the shirt. That was my regular job. "Looks all right. One side is a little off, but no one will notice." The difference between the right and left side was about one hundredth of an inch.

"Keep looking," she said. I looked some more.

"The cuffs are unbuttoned," I said.

"I forgot," she answered, and she opened her cuffs with a yank on each one. They were fastened with small snaps.

"Why the snaps?" I asked.

"I made the buttonhole too far from the edge. So I put the snaps on to make the cuffs close better. But I have to button them anyway so they look normal. I told you everything's wrong." She buttoned the cuffs and they looked perfect. Still, a tiny sound came out of her mouth. If not a wail, at least a yip. "Keep looking," she added.

I looked some more. "Looks fine," I said. Everything else looked fine.

"Oh, you," she said. "You're just being nice. Look at this." She pointed to her right shoulder.

"What?" I asked. I liked her shoulders. Right and left.

"I missed some stitches here, and it's crooked."

"It looks fine," I said. "Nothing looks crooked."

"Your eyes are crooked," she said, and she twisted her shoulder toward me and pointed again. "Right there." I didn't see a thing. "And everything else. The buttons don't look good and the collar's not even, and the pattern doesn't match at the seams."

"And everything else is wrong, too?" I asked. It all looked fine to me, but I'm the husband and sometimes my eyes are a little blurry after all the years we've been married.

"I'm not sure I can wear it."

"So give it to charity. Someone will want it." I looked at it again. If I were five feet tall and a petite woman, I would want it. It looked very Hawaiian.

"No, it's all wrong. The people would think it's a rag."

"People need rags," I said. Oh, oh.

"See, you think it's a rag."

"It's a Hawaiian rag," I said. Oh, oh, again.

"Hmmmm," she said looking at me. "Maybe you're right. It would make a neat Hawaiian rag. Maybe we should go to Hawaii again soon?" She smiled for the first time.

Now, no matter what I said then, I would eventually have to agree to another trip to Hawaii, all because of a shirt. I like Hawaii, of course, but the bill from our recent trip still lay on my desk. Now what to do? What to say?

"I like it the way it is," I said, after not-so-considerable thought.

"You do?"

"Absolutely," I said convincingly.

"Well, maybe you're right."

"So what are you going to do?"

"I still have some fabric. I think I'll make a skirt to match."

And that's how her wail turned into a matching outfit. And that's why I don't have to worry about going to Hawaii, at least for a while yet. Unless, of course, she decides it's too cold and foggy at home to wear her new outfit and starts wondering where we could go to find warm weather. Hmmmm.

46. Out of the Mouths of Babes

I want to thank you, Grandma," she said. She is three and a half and was on the telephone to her grandmother, my Darling Wife.

"I like my jacket," he said. He is five and just started kindergarten.

"I'm glad you like your clothes," my wife said.

This was at the beginning of the long-distance telephone call from our grandchildren to thank us for driving one hundred fifty miles and leaving off the clothes. The younger girl had been in preschool and the older boy had been at school when we had stopped by. The telephone call had come, according to our son-in-law, because the children wanted to thank the wonderful person who made the new outfits: a jacket and a shirt and a jumper and pajamas and shorts. And before they had gone to bed, the kids had begun trying everything on.

"I like the color," Shira said.

"I like the color, too," Shea said.

"Well, I made them so you would like them," Grandma said.

"I'm wearing them all to bed," Shira said.

"I'm wearing all mine to bed and all day tomorrow," Shea said.

"I want to wear mine forever," Shira said.

"I'm glad you like them so much," my wife said. We were both on the line, our attempt to watch television gladly interrupted, my comments limited that night to "Hello, I love you, too," and "Goodnight." But I listened to it all.

"Do you know my favorite color?" Shira asked.

"Yellow?" my wife guessed. It was hard keeping up. One week it was red, the next yellow, maybe blue.

"My favorite color is Lamb Chop," said Shira. The jumper was made out of Lamb Chop fabric.

"My favorite color is plaid," said Shea, who was wearing shorts of plaid, which I was told, made sewing the shorts a little difficult because Darling Wife had to match up every line at every seam, even though Shea might not know the difference. She would. Grandma wanted them to be perfect.

"We're glad you like the Lamp Chop and the plaid," Grandma said.

"They come to my knees," Shira said.

"Mine has a hood," Shea said.

"I like my knees to show," Shira said. "Can you see me?"

"I'll see you when we come down to visit next time," Grandma said. She had a lot of patience, and I had to change the telephone from my right ear to my left ear and rub my right ear until the circulation started again.

"I'm going to wear the pajamas to school," Shira said.

"You can't wear them to school," Shea said.

"Yes, I can. Can't I, Grandma?"

"You can wear your new jumper to school," Grandma said with the wisdom of Solomon.

"I like my clothes," said Shira, whose other outfit matched her brother's outfit.

"I have more clothes," said Shira.

"Do not."

"Do so," said Shira. "And I have pajamas and you don't."

"I have a hood," said Shea. I switched the telephone from my left ear back to my right ear.

"I made three outfits for each of you," said Grandma.

"I have three clothes," said Shea.

"I have three, too," said Shira.

"When are you going to make more?" Shira asked.

"Do you want more?" Grandma asked. Hah!

"I want pajamas too," said Shea. "Can you make shorts pajamas?"

"I'll make more for next time," said Grandma. And, of course, she will.

"Lots more?"

"Lots more," said Grandma.

"I love you, Grandma," Shira said.

"No, I love you," said Shea.

"I love you, too," said Grandma.

"Is Daddy there?" I asked, loudly enough so that if Daddy were anywhere within a mile of the telephone he would hear me. "I want to talk to Daddy," I said. I was hoping for Daddy to be very close by. I figured the telephone call, with the recesses the children took between talking on the telephone and discussing world events with each other, had taken a few hours and was going to cost our children about sixty-three thousand dollars. I really should have bought stock in AT&T when the grandkids were born.

"They really like the clothes," Daddy said. "They really want to tell you how much they like them."

"The doorbell's ringing," I said. "The house is on fire," I said.

"Let them say good-by," my delightfully patient Darling Wife said.

"Here, kids, Grandma wants to say good-by," Daddy said.

I settled in for the good-byes and the good-nights and I wondered how long it would be before I could get the circulation back into my ears. I also wondered how long it would be before my wife started going through her warehouse of fabric, or got out the patterns, or began threading the sewing machine and the serger. Grandma was probably already thinking about the color. What would please the grandchildren the most? Was it going to be birds or flowers or Sesame Street or Winnie the Pooh? She had fabric with all those designs. I didn't know.

But what I did know was that five minutes later we got another call. It was from another grandchild, Rachel, who lived two hundred fifty miles from us and was about to turn three. I wondered what she was going to talk about. Certainly not the clothes she was going to get for her birthday?

47. Size Me This

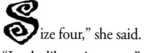ize four," she said.

"Looks like a six to me," I said. "But it could be a five or a seven."

"They don't have fives or sevens in this pattern."

"Why not?" I asked. I always asked wise questions when it came to sewing.

"It's a dumb pattern," she answered.

"Then why did you buy it?"

"It's a cute dress. I just couldn't tell from the package which way the sizes would run. It can say four and really be a six."

We were, of course, discussing the new dress she had just completed. She had tried a new pattern company, and she didn't know yet how the patterns were sized. Some patterns ran large and some ran small. Some ran away from common sense. Sizing problems could be solved more easily, we knew, if the grandchildren lived in our house, where she could have them try on the clothes after every stitch. But two grandchildren lived in Southern California, and two lived in Northern California, and we lived in Central California. And California is a big state. So, this Darling Wife of mine sews a bit blindly at times. Even when she has the measurements, the kids grow too fast and in all directions every day. So sometimes she screams at the pattern and wants to stomp on it or use it to line the trash can, but she's more sensible than to do anything, in my opinion, so logical.

"It's because the sizes never match their ages, and their ages are never the same," she said.

I didn't understand that exactly, but I know how frustrated we both were in Hawaii where cute outfits we wanted to buy came in two through four or six through eight, and we couldn't in any way look at them and guess which would fit a five-year-old. Even putting them side by side to compare them didn't help.

"So what are you going to do?" I asked, as she hung the new dress on a hanger.

"I'll send it to her and she can tell me if it's too big or too small. If it's too small, she can give it away. If it's too large, she can feed her daughter lots of bananas until she grows into it."

"Can't she just take it in?" Logic again.

"She could, but then I wouldn't have a reason to sew her a dress that fit exactly."

"And fitting exactly is important?" I asked in a sensible way.

"Sometimes it feels good when something I make fits exactly."

"It's because you don't want to do alterations either," I said, knowing her. She had too many new projects lined up to want to spend time redoing something already completed.

"I do alterations all the time," she said.

"You do not."

"While I'm working on a project I do. Afterward it's too late."

"Too late?" I wanted a complete explanation.

"What's done is done," she said firmly, but she had that look again. I could see sparkle in her eyes. "So do you think this will fit?" She held the dress up again.

"It'll fit someone," I said.

"Maybe we can drive down there so she can try it on."

"You just said you'd mail it."

"But it would be nice to visit them again."

"We were just there on Saturday," I said matter-of-factly. We were.

"But those were different outfits. And they were a little big. The last pattern ran small so I chose the next size and it's still a little big. Pattern companies should know better and make in-between sizes."

"You have a million patterns in those boxes. Couldn't you find one that had a better size?"

"Oh, you just reminded me," she said, her voice turning into a siren's song.

"What could I possibly have reminded you of?" I asked. I knew the trap she was setting.

"My patterns. I checked them all this morning. They're all sizes infant to toddlers. I need children's patterns. The grandkids are not toddlers any more."

"When did they change?" I asked.

"Don't try to weasel out of it," she said.

"Weasel out?" I'm not anything like a weasel.

"I need to buy a whole new collection of patterns. Sizes they can wear."

"You don't have any?"

"Well, a few of the pattern books have children's sizes up to twelve."

"So use them."

"I need more." Now she was breathing in a lustful manner, and just then she wasn't lusting for me.

"You need more?" My last chance of defense.

"What do you think? They're your grandkids, too."

"How much money are we talking?"

"Just enough."

"That can be a lot of money."

"You want them to go naked through the streets? Do you want them to believe they have no grandparents?"

"Their parents can buy them clothes." Sensible again.

"Store-bought? With no sizes they need on the racks? Never!"

"So when do you want to look for patterns?"

"Now's a fine time," she said.

And now it was.

OCTOBER

48. She Bought It for a Sarong

After she sorted out the bags of scraps and organized those she wanted to keep into neat piles and stored them away, she began going through some of the fabric she had brought back from our recent trip to Hawaii.

"I can't do it," she said to herself. She wasn't talking to me, as I was in the next room, but I heard her. She must have been talking to herself or to her fabric. She does both quite often, so it was no surprise to me to hear her. I had a decision to make then. I could go on with my own business and pay her words no attention, or I could, in reinforcing my role as a Darling Husband, ask her a question to draw her into conversation. I decided in favor of the latter.

"What can't you do?" I asked, as I moved closer to the doorway of her cutting room, that room off our kitchen that once was her office where she worked as a reading specialist and then became a pantry when she retired with me in May and now was a cutting room where she had replaced food on the shelves with fabric and used her old desk to trace patterns and cut the fabric. Whew!

"I can't do this to you," she said. She hadn't turned to face me but seemed to be talking to the fabric she held in her hands.

"What don't you want to do to me?" I asked, not really sure she was talking to me.

"What?" She turned to me.

"You said you didn't want to do something to me," I said. I looked at the fabric in her hands. It was a print with Hawaiian petroglyphs patterned against a rust-colored background. It was her favorite piece of fabric from the trip.

"Not you," she said. "I'm not talking to you."

"I didn't really think so," I said. "You were just having a conversation with your fabric."

She didn't respond at first, nor did she have to. That look of impatience she gave me spoke volumes. Then she turned back to the fabric. "You're too nice to cut up," she said.

Oh, so that was it. Every once in a while she went through this dilemma. She had a project in mind, she had the fabric in hand, but she turned from a killer wolf about to attack her project into a meek lamb with a tear in her eye and a lump in her throat. The fabric was too nice to cut up.

"You said when you bought it you were going to make a dress for yourself, one of those Hawaiian sarongs or some other kind of wrap-around."

"I changed my mind. You would too if you loved this fabric the way I do." Was I imagining it or was she caressing the fabric?

"So, are you just going to let it sit there on the shelf and not use it?" I knew she wouldn't. She had oohed and ahhed at it in the shop in Kauai and "just had to have it."

"It's my favorite fabric this year," she said. She rubbed it against her face. Still, she did seem attached to this one, cheek to selvage. And it was very attractive, even to my jaded eyes.

"Maybe you can cut off a small piece and frame it," I said, ducking as I did, for I knew wrath coming when I saw her flinch at the idea.

"I can't cut it, I could never cut it, but you've given me an idea. I can hang it on the wall."

"It's too big to hang on any of our walls," I said. I was practical. We had no walls left uncovered in the house to hang even a dust mote.

"Well, then," she began, but then she hesitated, looked at me, looked beyond me, and then she smiled. She grinned. She was a cat spying a bird in a very low tree.

"What?" I asked, seeing that look. "What are you thinking?" I said with trepidation hanging between my words.

"Help me clear the table," she said.

"What?"

"Help me clear the table. We can use this as a tablecloth."

"A tablecloth?"

"That's what I said. It might just fit."

"You can't put plates and glasses and food on that," I exclaimed. "One stain and you'll...." I had no words to express what she might do if her Oscar-winning fabric became stained. And as sloppy as I was at the table—it was too horrible to contemplate.

"Plastic," she said.

"What?" How did this questioning word become my only vocabulary?

"We can cover it in vinyl. Remember the roll of clear vinyl we bought to cover the table when the grandchildren were babies?"

"I remember it," I said. It was rolled up somewhere in the back of the garage.

"We can cover the fabric with the plastic and I can see it every time we eat and I won't have to cut it." She sparkled, as she began to clear the table. She began to remove the lazy Susan, the napkins, the sugar, all of the table reappearing as she worked.

And that is why now, at every meal, we sit down to the most exotic, most beautiful, most uncut piece of fabric she owns, which did happen to fit the table without cutting it. Seeing it there makes each meal a banquet. Now if we only had some palm trees and a tropical breeze.

49. The Patient's Wife

She watched as the doctor unstapled me. "Hmmm," she said.

"What do you mean by that?" I asked. I lay still on the bed, as the doctor removed each staple and dropped it onto a gauze pad by my side.

"I was just wondering how much better staples are than stitches," she said.

"For my incision or for your sewing?" I asked.

"I'm not thinking about sewing. I haven't thought about sewing for five days."

She was telling the truth. She had been with me in my hospital room all that week after my surgery. She had not brought any sewing. She had not mentioned sewing. She was there to be with me. "I can sew later," she had said, as she sat by my bedside that first day.

"Staples wouldn't work in sewing," she now said. "Not even for basting."

"Probably not," said the doctor, as he finished removing the last staple.

"You could've used buttons or snaps," I said. "That way if you left something inside...."

"He's ready to go home now," said the doctor.

"Or a zipper," I said, while I had the chance.

"You're ready to go home now," my wife said to me rather forcefully.

"May I go home now?" I asked the doctor.

"The sooner the better," he said. "But follow my directions. You need to take care of yourself," he said to me. To my wife he said, "You'll have your hands full, you know."

"I know. I'll take care of him," my sweetheart said.

The doctor nodded and left, my wife helped me dress, an orderly wheelchaired me out of the hospital, and we were on our way home. Home.

That was three weeks ago. Three weeks of recuperation for me, getting back to normal, eating again, sleeping without interruptions by a thousand nurses checking my vital signs a thousand times a day. Now only my Darling Wife was checking me all day long. That is, when she wasn't sewing.

"I have a backlog," she had said when we first arrived home.

"A backlog of sewing?" I had asked. Maybe I was still hallucinating from the effects of the antibiotics or the pain pills. I should have known better than to have asked *that* question.

"Six months worth," she had said.

"You were away for only five days."

"That's the same as six months in sewing time," she had said.

And it was. Once I was safely in bed, fed, washed, and as comfortable as I could be, she left my bedside and went the eight feet into the sewing room. From then until now the sewing machine has not stopped.

First it was the curtains for our grandson, Shea. He was about to turn six and decided his room needed jungle curtains with lions and tigers and other creatures. Our daughter bought the fabric, brought it a hundred and fifty miles to our house, and promised that during her visit while I was in the hospital, she was going to help with the sewing. Strangely, with my wife at the hospital most of the time, that sewing did not get done.

"I've never done real curtains before," my wife said to me.

"You can do them," I said encouragingly.

"Not until I'm sure you're all right."

"I'll get better faster if I hear you sewing," I said. I didn't tell her I could see her anxiety during the days she wasn't sewing. The anxiety she felt for my health and my future were one important thing. But the trembling of her heart for the touch of fabric again, for the adjustment of the tension on her machines, for the gentle rumbling of her serger cutting along the fabric, that was there as well.

"Are you sure?" she asked.

"I'll yell if I need you," I said. And I did yell a lot. And she was always there. She was there with a needle and thread in her hand, a pincushion, the lining for the curtains, the panels for the curtains. All the time I was being properly attended to, the curtains were getting similar care.

And after the curtains were done, ironed, and put in boxes to take south with us on our first visit when I could travel again, she went to work on the rest of her "backlog."

Next there was the bedspread for our grandson who wanted his bed covered with leopards. Then, for the first time in months, she made something for herself, a sleeveless blouse for spring. "I needed a blouse," she said when she finished.

She made a ruffled dress to give to one of our granddaughters. She made another ruffled dress for our other granddaughter. Fair is fair. No envy allowed.

She made a shirt. She made a skirt. She made and made and made. (Unbelievably, her mile-high pile of stash did not seem to go down at all. Was she sneaking out to the fabric shop while I napped? Nah, she wouldn't leave me alone, would she?)

It's been three weeks now. I am able to feed myself, go for walks around the neighborhood, and otherwise take care of myself. She is still sewing.

And she was right about the backlog. After all this time, she is just barely catching up to the work she is certain she missed during those five days. By the new year, I expect, she'll be all caught up. Maybe by then I'll ask her to sew something for me, maybe something with staples.

50. Lullaby and Good Night

She had begun sewing at three in the morning to get the last project completed before our son, his wife, and our granddaughter visited the next day, and many sewing hours later I passed the door to her sewing room. I looked in to see my Darling Wife sitting at her machine. As I looked at her, I became very aware of the hum and click of the sewing machine and the faint hum of her deep breathing in rhythm with the machine. At first I thought she was working out her next move, her mind busy with deciding which stitch to use next, what length to make the stitch, how wide to make the stitch. But no, she was sound asleep at her sewing machine, her head down on the side of her right arm, her left arm draped across the flowered cotton fabric she was working on.

It was not the first time she had fallen asleep at the machine. It used to be that I would go and shake her gently, telling her she had fallen asleep, and she would open a sleepy eye and tell me that she wasn't sleeping at all. "I'm only resting my eyes," she would always say.

I had given up trying to awaken her. Somehow her body knew when it was time to move, when it was time to sew again. This time, however, though her body and mind were somewhat unconscious, she was still sewing. I wouldn't have known except that the fabric under her left arm was moving, the feed dogs moving it through the machine, the needle going up and down. She was sewing asleep. I looked down under the machine and her right foot was heavy on the foot pedal.

I moved to the machine to shut it off, afraid she would sew her arm into the dress she was making for our granddaughter. She might even sew her head onto the fabric. However, as the machine stopped, the silence awakened her.

"What are you doing?" she asked groggily, no doubt puzzled by my audacity.

"What are *you* doing?" I asked in reply. Did she know she was asleep?

"I'm sewing here," she said. She lifted her head off her arm, her arm dark red where her head had pressed the blood out of circulation.

"Well, I'm saving your life," I said. "You were sound asleep and about to become a very realistic appliqué."

"I wasn't asleep," she said. "I was just resting my eyes."

"You were asleep and about to sew yourself into a nightmare."

"Well, even if I was asleep, and I'm not admitting that I was, I still can sew in my sleep." At that she looked at the fabric that had passed through her machine. She held up the fabric for me to see.

"What's it supposed to be?" I asked.

"It's a muumuu," she said. "It's not quite finished yet."

"It looks like a badly sewn pup tent, or maybe it's a vampire's cape," I suggested. It could have been either.

First she frowned at me, a very mean looking "mind-your-own-business" frown. Then she looked closely at the stitching. I think she realized then that about a thousand of the stitches were not hers and that the would-be dress was sewn by some goblin that had been inhabiting her sleeping body. It was apparent that the goblin had not been following any known dress pattern.

"I don't think it's too bad," she tried.

"It's very bad," I said diplomatically.

"I can rip out some of the stitches," she said. "They're just a little off."

"Or you can go back to sleep and let the machine finish it," I offered helpfully.

"I'm too tired to sleep now," she said. "I think I'll see what I can do to fix this." She felt along the stitching with both hands. "It's actually a good tight stitch," she said.

"Are you complimenting the sewing machine?" I asked.

"It deserves some credit," she said. As she talked she reached into the drawer nearby and pulled out a seam ripper. Before I could object that it was dangerous to have a sharpened piece of steel in her hand in her half-asleep condition, she began cutting at the stitching.

"This could wait until another time, when you're awake," I said, but she obviously didn't hear me. Or she did hear me and paid me no heed. She ripped at the fabric.

There was nothing more I could say or do. I left her and went outside and went for a walk and looked for the moon in the sky, but it was gone. When I returned a while later, I went to her sewing room. She sat rigid at her sewing table hard asleep, her fabric in one hand, her seam ripper in the other. At least the sewing machine was off. I went to her slumbering body and removed the ripper from her right hand. I removed the fabric from her left hand. All the bad stitches had been ripped out. How she did that, I would never know.

Though I was gentle, though I was quiet and careful, my movements still awakened her.

"What?" she said in new confusion. She yawned a slight but perky little yawn.

"Do you know what you were doing?" I asked, as I pulled her from the chair and led her somnolent body from the sewing machine to the bed. There she collapsed back into dreamland. But just before she did, for one brief moment, she opened an eye and looked up at me and answered my question.

"I was just resting my eyes," she said.

51. Airborne

"Airborne Express," she said softly, but her tone expressed worry. She was standing by the kitchen window looking out at the street.

"What about Airborne Express?" I asked. I looked out past her to the empty street.

"They should have been here by now."

"Why? What are we expecting?" I asked. Dumb question.

"My order," she said. "Where is the truck?"

"What order?" I could guess.

"Oh, just some notions I needed," she said.

"Some notions," I repeated, mocking her with my voice, but she paid me no attention. Her notions kept Airborne Express in business. Her fabrics kept UPS drivers from becoming unemployed. Her patterns kept the US Post Office out of debt.

Our house had become mail-order paradise as soon as she had begun her winter sewing campaign. She had begun her winter campaign when the department stores displayed the new winter children's fashions.

"I can make that," she had said, as she looked at each outfit on the rack. Spring practice was over. It was now time for the regular season. "All I need is some cute fabric, a few notions, a few nice patterns."

First, of course, we visited our town's three fabric stores. Nothing we saw satisfied her. Then the new catalogs began to come in the mail. Then the trucks came. Then there was the sight of her at the window each day.

"Why don't you sew something while you're waiting?" I asked genially.

"Why don't you call Airborne for me?" she replied, her voice swift and sure.

"They never tell you when they're coming. They have to deliver to a lot of customers," I explained, though she knew that.

"They're always here by now," she said. She was a regular and she knew from experience. She turned from the counter and moved quickly to the front door. She opened the door and went outside. I watched her through the window. She stood on the curb looking up and down the street. Now I had a dilemma. Should I call her back in? Should I knock her over the head and drag her back in? Should I call Airborne Express?

By the time the van finally pulled to the curb in front of our house, the sky had clouded up, the regular mail had come and gone, and my sweet, gentle, calm wife had become manic as she paced the kitchen, took to washing all the dishes twice, made enough salads to last a week, rearranged a pantry of canned goods, called Airborne Express twice ("I'm sure our truck will be there soon"), and ate every leftover in the refrigerator. I tried to help, I really did, but she was an addict, hooked on deliveries. She needed her fix.

Have you ever seen the aftermath of a violent storm? It was that way that day. She scribbled her signature, yanked the package out of the driver's hand, and tore back into the house. She became a whirlwind, as she carried the package into the kitchen, where she ripped it open with the force of a dozen tornadoes. I could only stand out of her way and wait until she ran off with her prize back to the sewing room. I cleaned up the debris, wiped shredded wrapping off the counter, and swept the floor. Then I went after her.

Mr. Hyde could not have changed back to Dr. Jekyll so quickly. She sat humming at her sewing machine, calm and at peace with her world. She had new thread and needles and what seemed to be a hundred other notions spread out before her. She hummed and looked at them and hummed some more. I waited.

Finally, I coughed quietly, and she turned to see me. She smiled, ecstatic. "The driver promised to be on time next time," she said.

"I hope so," I said. I kissed her on the top of her head. "Oh, please, I hope so," I prayed.

52. Stick It to Me

"Hon, have you seen my address labels?" I asked after fumbling around my desk looking for them. I had just paid the week's bills and my envelopes were all addressed and stamped. I had only to stick on the return address labels and I could get them into the mail.

"What?" she called from the sewing room.

"Our return address labels. I can't find them."

"Oh, I have them," she said. "I was using a few."

I went into her sewing room. "You finally caught up on your mail?" I asked.

"No," she said. She handed me the large roll of labels.

"Then what?" I asked.

"I just needed a few," she said. Her tone warned me not to ask any more questions. Knowing her, I didn't.

I went back to my desk, finished with the envelopes, and went outside to put them in the mail box. Too late, the mail had already come. I took the delivered mail back into the house. I put my outgoing mail away to go out the next day and began sorting through the new mail, mostly advertisements and catalogs. One large envelope was addressed to my Darling Wife, and it had a "Free Gift Inside" label on it. We rarely ever respond to the gimmicks and come-ons that invade our house daily, and though this one advertised the "deal of a lifetime," it would be no exception.

"This is for you," I said. "Free gift inside." I handed her the large envelope and watched as she opened it.

"How did they know?" she asked, as she tore though the thousand or so ads inside and pulled out a sheet of yellow smiley stickers.

"How did they know you wanted yellow smiley stickers?" I asked. Did she want them? Of course. When the grandkids came, we always handed them over so they could stick them on everything in sight. Fortunately, our grandchildren were all born after the advent of removable stickers. When our own children were young, all stickers stuck. That is why painters charged us extra. That is why house guests smiled at seeing rabbits and bears and kittens and dragons stuck to all our walls, all our furniture. That is why we spent most of our time, which should have been leisure time, unsticking the stickers. Fortunately, years ago we discovered that lighter fluid took off most stickers, those on packages we bought at the store and those on ninety-nine percent of our house.

"I really needed them yesterday," she said. I looked at her but said nothing. I knew she would continue. "But I can use them next time."

"You're going to use them?" I asked. "What about the grandkids?"

"They're getting too old for them," she said. "Besides, these will save you a lot of money."

"How do I save money?" I asked. We never bought stickers. We had always had a house full of stickers from my wife's teaching days.

"I don't have to buy them from the catalog."

"What catalog?" I didn't remember any catalog.

"All the sewing catalogs. They sell them for sewing."

"They sell smiley stickers for sewing?"

"Not smiley stickers, but they're a little like them. They have little markings so I can line up the fabric when I'm sewing. I also use stickers instead of dots when patterns call for dots and tell me to sew between the dots. I put them on the front side of fabric when I can't tell which side is the front side. I use them to mark where to stop sewing when I have to leave a seam open. I use them for everything. But they got to be very expensive, even when I used them over again, which is hard to do as they get so linty."

"Linty?" I was baffled, but that was not new.

"Come on, I'll show you," she said. She took me over to where she had been cutting out the fabric, where she had the patterns all cut

12 Months of Sewing

and ready. "I used to buy them, but then I ran out and used some of the blank stickers, like the ones on the sewing machine that tell me what needle I have in. Like the Post-its I use for helpful hints from people on the Internet. I just used some of them and cut them up and made marks on them myself. But I ran out of everything this morning." She ended looking up at me to prompt her.

"So?" I prompted.

"So, I used the address labels. But I almost ruined the skirt I was making."

"You used the address labels to make a skirt and almost ruined it?" I almost had it, but not quite.

She didn't answer me for the moment. Instead she pointed out the skirt she was putting together. In about a dozen places on the fabric, I could see small triangles cut out of the return address labels. Some were torn. Some were ripped, showing only adhesive.

"And?" I asked. No fool was I to jump to any conclusions.

"And I forgot they weren't removable, and it's going to take a while to get them off the fabric."

"And now you're going to use the smiley labels that came in the mail because they are removable." It wasn't a question.

"I didn't have any more bunny stickers or flower stickers or even those return address stickers that come with the mail from all the charities. I didn't have anything else to use. But now I have enough stickers to last me until we go shopping again."

"We're going shopping for stickers?"

"As soon as I use up the smiley stickers."

At the rate she was sewing, that would probably be no later than that afternoon. I would have time to go through the rest of the mail. Maybe there would be other stickers. Maybe.

NOVEMBER

WOOLLY NYLON TWIN-SET
M E M O R I A L S

53. The Grass Is Always Greener

We'll need to rent a truck," she said.

"A truck?"

"A Ryder or a U-Haul. We can fill it up and then drive back."

"That's three thousand miles," I said. I wondered why I was in this conversation. We were standing in front of a wholesale fabric store in the garment district of New York. It was the second day of our visit to New York, and we had spent the morning on the top of the Empire State Building. She hadn't mentioned buying any fabric as we looked down over Manhattan. Of course, I knew it was inevitable that we would find ourselves in a fabric shop or quilting shop or a button shop or a notions shop or a trim shop. Everyone had warned us about the abundance of shops in New York City. But I had not anticipated block after block of trim shops and button shops and fabric shops. The day before we had been standing in the crown of the Statue of Liberty, and she had sworn that all we would do was sightsee for the next ten days. Only if we accidentally happened upon a store would we go in, she promised. Hah!

"Well, we can't carry all that fabric and all those notions on the plane," she said.

"What fabric?" I asked. She pointed into the store where it seemed miles of shelving carried millions of bolts of fabric. Then she pointed next door where through the window were displayed ten zillion buttons. And beyond that was a trim store where a universe of trim of every kind hung from the walls in dizzying rows and rows of dazzling assortments.

"Well, if we rented a truck we could go in there and get anything we wanted," she said. I stared at her. I replayed her voice in my then exploding brain to see if I could detect any humor in her words, but she seemed dead serious. "And later when we go up to Vermont, we could stop everywhere and get everything and we could drive back to California with enough of a stash to get in a book of records."

"No," I said firmly. My word solid. Steel. Emphatic. No wishy-washiness in my tone. A man for all seasons in my declaration.

"No?" she asked.

"We are not going to rent a truck. We are not going into this store or that store or any store. We are not going to think about buying anything except a T-shirt that says New York." I was Moses handing down the tablets. But I needed only one commandment. "Thou shalt not shop for fabric on vacation," I said.

"We're not on vacation," she replied. "We're retired. You can't take a vacation when you're retired."

"Thou shalt not shop for fabric in New York, Massachusetts, Vermont, Connecticut, New Hampshire, or Pennsylvania," I said, amending the commandment.

"But, but," she sputtered.

"You can look, you can swoon, you can drool, but you can't buy," I said.

"All right, Honey," she said way too sweetly to be sincere, but I accepted her acquiescence.

So we went into the store and looked. And looked and looked. Then we were out on the street again. And we were empty-handed. Miracle of miracles.

"Pooh," she said.

"Pooh?" I questioned.

"They didn't have anything special in there I couldn't get back home."

"What about the price?" I asked. I knew the joy of getting a bargain.

"We would have to buy about a thousand yards to get the right price. We don't need that. Let's go."

"How about the button shop, the other shops?"

"We'll go in, but only for a minute. It's too nice out to go shopping. And I want to go to the top of the World Trade Center."

"Are you all right?" I asked, feeling her brow for some fever.

"I'm all right," she said. But I was not really sure. We went down the block, looked in windows, stepped quickly in and out of shops, and finally came to a stop at the intersection.

"So, what just happened back there?" I asked.

"Nothing happened. I just don't need anything today. Tomorrow may be different."

"And the truck?"

"What truck?"

"The eighteen-wheel U-Haul," I said.

"Don't be silly. Why would we need a truck for a T-shirt?" she said. The traffic signal turned to "Walk" then and we walked ... and walked ... and walked. I hoped I would never be silly again.

54. Color Me a Rainbow

Hon, what's this," I said, as I held the piece of underwear up to her face.

"Your shorts, dear," she said to me.

"I know they are my shorts, but they are purple."

"Yes, they are," she said.

"Why are they purple?" I asked.

"Because," she said. She didn't have to say anything more. I knew why they were purple. They were purple for the same reason I had pink socks instead of white, blue handkerchiefs instead of white, yellow T-shirts instead of white. It was why I had on a pair of mint green briefs.

"You went shopping again," I said. It wasn't a question. It wasn't an accusation. It was a fact that I announced and I didn't need her to confirm it. "And you bought purple fabric," I said. That too was not a question, not a guess. It was as certain as my knowing she would be sewing some time that day.

"Do you want me to bleach it out?" she asked.

"No, purple's fine," I said. I could live with purple shorts. I just had to be careful not to wear them under my white pants. That is, if I had any white pants left.

During the past year my life has become a tie-dyed wonderland, a spectrum of colors. At times I thought we were back in the sixties, when she experimented on the children's clothes, giving in to their demands to be tiny hippies, as they went off to elementary school dressed in a tumult of color. But I was no hippie. I had not asked her to fill a tub with boiling water and exotic dyes or carefully bind up and dip my clothes.

No, I was a rainbow of fashion because she had taken up sewing again.

"Do I have anything white left to wear, Dear?" I asked her poetically.

"You might have some, Hon," she said. Of course, that meant I might not.

"You could have used some scraps," I said to her. I had said that to her before.

"I ran out," she said. "Besides, I didn't expect it this time."

"So, I have purple shorts."

"They're cute," she said. She always said my clothes were cute.

"At my age I don't need to be cute," I said. "I need to be clean, sterile, white."

"You're just an old fuddy-duddy," she said.

"A fuddy-duddy?"

"You need more color in your life," she said.

"I have plenty of color in my life. Thanks to your sewing, my life has become a kaleidoscope of color."

"I'm just doing the right thing," she said. "I have to test the fabric."

What she was saying was that she paid attention to all the sewing books she has read, all the sewing magazines, all the helpful hints on the Internet. And that advice told her to pre-wash all her new fabrics in the same manner they were going to be washed after she turned the fabric into some magical piece of clothing to wear. And when she brought home new fabric, which was often, she ran the frayed edges, the selvageless sides through her serger so the fabric's edges wouldn't fray, wouldn't ravel or unravel. (Now, why are there two words to mean the same thing?)

"Not all fabric is well-dyed," she said then, knowing absolutely what I was thinking.

"I know, Darling. I am living proof of that." And of course whenever she washed fabric that she suspected might contain colors that would run amuck, she always threw in a piece of white fabric to test how colorfast it might be. And when she didn't have a handy piece of scrap fabric, what better than my shorts, my T-shirts, any of my clothes that might, in her eyes, be tired of being white? It was color roulette for me. If the color held, I got to wear white a little longer. If not ... well ... I'd have more pretty clothes. That's why I stay inside the house a lot. No one wants to see an old hippie walking the streets these days.

55. Lost and Found

She was going through her scrap piles as I came into the sewing room. "What are you doing now?" I asked. I have long ago learned that there was no way for me to know what she was doing by watching what she was doing. I had guessed wrong too often. If I had guessed then that she was looking for a scrap of fabric to take with her to buy matching thread, I would have been wrong. If I had guessed she was looking through her scrap piles because she had an idea to make a bra out of the scraps, I would have been wrong. So I asked her.

"I'm looking for the collar," she said. She finished with the scrap piles and started looking through the trash basket.

"You lost a collar?" I asked.

"I didn't lose it. I'm just looking to see where I put it," she said.

"What?" I asked. What she had just said no doubt made perfect sense to her. I was the dunce. Though I knew what a collar was. The word derives from Middle English *coler*, which derived from Old French *colier*, from Latin *collare*, from *collum* meaning neck.

In a moment she was finished with the trash. She looked around her serger. "It's the collar for the new dress," she said, as if that would explain the world to me.

"Do you want me to help you look?" I asked. I did want to be helpful.

"You can go look in the kitchen. I haven't looked there yet."

"The kitchen. You want me to look for your collar in the kitchen?"

"It might be there."

"I might find a colander. Would that do?" I said very playfully.

"Very funny. I said collar. It's blue, just like this dress I'm making." She held up the collarless dress. It was sleeveless with two large pockets, and it was all done except for the collar.

"How would it get in the kitchen?" I asked. "Did it run away?"

"Go," she commanded, as she bent herself at the knees to look under the sewing table.

I went into the kitchen, looked around, and opened the refrigerator. (Why not? I've found thread in there before, so why not a collar?) I searched all of the appliances and all of the cupboards, but no collar. I returned to the scene of the crime. There had to be a crime. Maybe I could collar a collar thief.

She was lying on the floor looking under the bed. Her right arm was stretched out of sight. "Not in the kitchen," I said.

"Try the bathroom," she said, her words echoing under the bed, as she pressed her head under the box spring to look into the darkness.

"All right," I obeyed. I searched the bathroom, the hamper, the shower, the medicine cabinet, the toilet bowl. If I was looking for a collar I now thought didn't exist, why not look everywhere I knew it wouldn't be?

"I give up," she said, as I returned to find her brushing lint and dust from her clothes. "I'll just make another one."

"How long will that take?"

"Less time than it would to look for it any more," she said. She seemed cheery then, as if nothing much had happened, as if she doubted whether she would have to call in the FBI or pay a ransom.

"Well, I'm thinking of posting a reward," I said, hoping to cheer her even more.

"I'll offer a reward to someone to kidnap you," she said cheerfully. "Now go. I have to sew a new collar."

I zipped my lip, turned and went swiftly to a safer part of the house.

Later, at dinner, she came in wearing the new dress. The dress was complete with a collar, and whether it was a new one or the old one, I couldn't tell. But the dress did look good on her. We were going to have a happy dinner.

We had part of a happy dinner. As we began dinner, she sprinkled some pepper on her salad. Some of it drifted toward her nose, and she began to sneeze. She caught the first sneeze by placing her finger under her nose, but a few seconds later she wrinkled her nose and began a real sneeze. As she began that sneeze, she instinctively reached into the pocket of her new dress for a Kleenex, and she brought one to her nose to catch the sneeze. It was a funny tissue. It was blue, and it was curved like a human neck, and it looked just like the collar on her dress.

"Nice tissue," I said admiringly.

She looked at me a moment, then looked at what she held in her hand and began to laugh. "I must have put it in the pocket so I wouldn't lose track of it," she explained without embarrassment.

"Must have," I said.

"Well, if someone collarnaps the new one from my dress, I'll have a spare."

She sneezed again, but she was ready for it. So was the collar.

"Bless you," I said.

56. Creative

She had talked about it on occasion, telling me about the sewers who were creative, who could make something original out of something old and tired and boring. But she had never dared to take the chance herself. "I'm just not creative," she said. That she had been creative in marrying me, rearing our three children, teaching reading to students with learning disabilities, these to her were not things that required creativity. "Just common sense," she'd say. Adding a frill to the pocket of a blouse, trimming a jacket with beads, attaching ribbons to a hat, these things she considered being creative.

"Everything you make is creative," I said. "I don't think you've ever followed a pattern the way it was designed."

"That wasn't being creative. That was not being able to follow the directions." She pouted.

And that was the way our occasional conversation on the subject went. So it was a big surprise to me when I went into her sewing room the other day and thought a hurricane had hit it. With the public's current interest in movies and documentaries about tornadoes and cyclones and twisters, I thought she had been acting out a storm. There was chaos in the room. On the cutting table, the bookcase, the sewing machine table, the floor were spread out patterns, sewing books, tracing paper, scissors, spools of thread. Now, ordinarily, she was a neat-freak, but not now. No doubt the room had been invaded by some force beyond imagination.

"What happened?" I asked casually. No sense rushing into my concern.

"Nothing happened. I've been sewing," she said. She held a small square of blue cotton knit in one hand and a small appliqué of a rabbit in the other.

"Then what's all this?" I said, spreading my arms to take in the clutter in the room.

"Oh, well, I didn't have a pattern for what I decided to make." She moved toward the ironing board where several strips of cloth were cut and pinned to pieces of tracing paper. "I'm using pieces of several patterns," she said.

"Are you allowed to do that?" That morning she had been telling me about the arguments on the Internet about copyright laws.

"Of course. All the fuss was about whether a person could use a copyrighted pattern and then sell the garment. What I'm making won't be for sale."

"And what are you making?" I knew she wanted me to ask.

"Just a simple little baby jacket. I don't have a pattern in the house, so I took a sweater pattern and a shirt pattern and a couple of other patterns, and I'm experimenting to see if I can make something."

"And can you make something?"

"I'm just experimenting," she said.

Shaking my head at the mess in the room, I left her to her experiment. I had my own experiment to do in the kitchen with the refrigerator and food and my stomach.

I ate and watched the news and made out some checks to pay some bills (including bills for fabric and notions and thread, bills which seemed to come to the house daily). Then I wandered to the back of the house to see what had become of my Darling Wife.

The room was still a jumble of books and patterns and fabric, but in the middle of it all my wife stood about a foot taller than usual. She was beaming, a look of pride on her face that made the room bright around her. She held out a blue baby jacket trimmed in white with tiny red buttons and a white ribbed bottom. It was beautiful. "You made that?" I said, remarkably casual.

"Of course I made that. Do you see anyone in this room with me?"

"But you didn't follow a pattern, did you? You created that yourself, didn't you?"

"Well, I told you I didn't have the pattern I needed."

"So you made your own?"

"I just said that."

"And you were creative, weren't you?"

"I...." She stopped, her lips not moving, her face flushed. "Well, I, well, maybe."

"Creative!" I said. "Creative. Creative. Creative." I like to make my point. "You did it all by yourself, so don't ever tell me you aren't creative."

She stared at the jacket she held. She smiled again. "It is cute, isn't it?" she said.

"Not as cute as you, right now, but it'll do." She grinned with sewing happiness. "Now, are you going to clean up the mess in here?"

"Mess?" She looked around. "What mess? A creative person has to have some freedom to create. Creative people aren't always neat, you know."

"Yes, I know," I said. Creative people! Yes, I certainly did know.

57. Lull-a-Buy

I'm out of thread," she said.

"Nonsense," I said. "You've never been out of thread in your life."

"I need some woolly nylon," she said.

"You have enough woolly nylon to girdle the earth," I said. I passed in front of where she stood in the sewing room. She did look distraught. But I knew where the thread was. I opened her well-marked box of decorative threads. I pointed out that she had a spool of every color known to the human race.

"I need more," she said.

"Why?" Now that's a common question. I ask it often. I am looking for an explanation when I ask that question. My mind is befuddled when I ask that question. I want my mind to be clear and comprehend everything. Is that asking too much?

She pointed to the thread. "I have only one of each color," she said.

"So?" That's probably my second most common question. I use it to tell her that I am not quite clear as to her answer.

"I can do only the upper looper," she said.

"And?" That's my third most common question. It's to push the conversation along. It's to elicit more information, so I can *fully* understand her answer.

"That's not woolly enough," she said.

"Huh?" That's sort of a question, but it's more a sound created by a confused mind.

"I need to have woolly nylon in both the upper looper and lower looper. That way I can make the ends of the sleeves nice and fuzzy. The threads have to be the same color."

"A-ha!" I understood, but I needed confirmation. "So you need one more spool of every color of woolly nylon you have?"

"You got it, Buster," she said. She had never called me Buster before. She must have been storing it up for just the right occasion. It must be a word that was otherwise reserved for some dull husband who didn't understand sewing needs.

"Now?" I asked. I don't know what number on the list that question is, but she always answers it the same way.

"Yes," she said, and we were on our way to the fabric store.

Two things happened that day. I learned about the need for really fuzzy sewing, and I found out what it was like for her to be in shopping heaven.

The store was empty! It was ten o'clock in the morning on a Wednesday, and, except for the three clerks putting up stock, the store was empty. I had never been in an empty fabric store before. Darling Wife had never been in an empty fabric store before. "Something's wrong," she said. She sniffed the air. She looked down the aisles. She looked behind displays. And then she purred in absolute delight and contentment. The store was empty. It really, really was.

That was the good news. The bad news was that she didn't know what do. It was a fantasy land and she wasn't prepared for the fantasy. I nudged her back into reality. "Woolly nylon," I said.

"Oh, yes," she cooed, and we went to find the thread. It was on sale for 25 percent off. "Oh, yes," she said again. Then she looked around and around. She turned so quickly, she began to spin.

"The store's still empty," I said, even though the one thing she came for, the woolly nylon, was on sale. Why weren't there customers fighting her for the thread?

She gulped and shook herself; then, she gathered her senses and pulled spools of woolly nylon off the shelves. She got spools to match all her existing colors, and then she got two spools of each color she didn't have. When she was finished, the cart was half-full. (She's an optimist. It would never be half-empty.) But the store was still empty. "Maybe I'll look for a small piece of fabric to make the grandkids something," she said.

"There's no one in line at the checkout stand," I said. There was no clerk there either. "Now would be a good time to check out," I said. Oh, foolish me.

"In just a minute," she said.

In that minute she circled the store like a tornado, found seven bolts of fabric, filled her cart, and pushed her hoard to the cutting counter. There, a woman looked up from where she was rolling remnants and smiled. My wife pushed the fabric onto the counter and told her how much fabric she wanted. Six of the fabrics were for the grandkids; one was for her. The clerk began cutting.

"Where is everyone?" my wife finally asked.

"Oh, we're just having a lull," the clerk said. She kept cutting and folding.

"How often does that happen?" I asked.

"Oh, this is the first time since I've been working here," she said.

"How long is that?" I asked. Darling Wife was taking the folded fabric and putting it carefully into the cart.

"Eighteen years," the clerk said. "I never expected a lull."

"I can understand that," I said. Poor woman. She never expected a lull. Well, neither did my wife. She was almost faint from the experience. She kept putting the fabric in her cart, caressing it, and looking around the store.

In a few minutes we were done at the cutting counter and in line at the checkout stand. Wrong. There was no line. I looked around. I saw a clerk putting prices on a new shipment of thread. I walked over to her and said, "We're ready."

The clerk nodded, followed me back to the cash register, rang up the sale, and bagged our purchases.

As we paid, this clerk looked at both of us, smiled broadly, and explained, "We're having a lull, you know," and then she was gone, back to her roll of price stickers.

"What just happened?" Darling Wife asked, as we drove away.

"We got the woolly nylon," I said. "And about a million dollars worth of stuff we didn't come for."

"I sure liked that lull," she said dreamily. "I wonder if that will ever happen again."

"Maybe when you need to sew fuzzy again," I said.

"I'll always remember this day," she said, and she laid her head back against the head rest and sighed a very contented smile. I kept thinking about the bill. I wondered if there would ever be a lull in her shopping.

58. Marriage Vows

Now she says that as I am at the computer so much, writing those exaggerated stories of her sewing life, I have too much time on my hands and that I should do something more practical, such as sorting out all her scraps by shape and color, vacuuming Joseph's Coat of Many Colors (what she calls the accumulation of lint decorating her serger) or refolding all the airy-thin patterns and putting them in their separate pattern envelopes without shredding them (much, much worse than refolding any map).

"This is practical. We now have twenty-seven sewing lists. Who downloads them for you? Who reads and separates and files all the sewing postings by subject? Who waits in the fabric store to keep a place in the cashier's line while you're busy at the cutting table with fifty-four bolts of fabric? Who finds that impossible-to-find size six hundred/forty-eight universal double needle with the three eyes? Who fights off the other customers for the two yards of remnant holiday burlap on the sale table?"

"Well, any husband would do that," she began. She paused, thought for a moment, and added, "It was in the third paragraph—" She left her words floating in mid-air.

"What third paragraph?" I knew she would tell me exactly what paragraph.

"In our marriage vows. Remember, it's where you promised to be a partner in love and sewing."

"Love *and* sewing? I don't remember anything like that. And besides, that was almost thirty-six years ago."

"It was there. And there was the seventh paragraph, too."

"What seventh paragraph?" Did I sign some sewer's ten commandments?

"Where you promised to honor me and my notions."

"You didn't say they were sewing notions."

"Well, they were. And thinking of that, call the fabric store and ask what time their sale begins."

"What sale?"

"I think it's in honor of the end of something, or maybe it's the beginning of Leap Year. Or maybe it's the sale of sales celebrating the protection of the whales—or was it lobsters? It's on the calendar." She has the calendar boldly marked with every sale in every store within twenty-five miles of us.

"I will, as soon as I finish here," I said, surrendering again. I turned back to the computer.

"Well, all right, but don't take too long, and don't make anything up."

"I'll just tell the truth," I promised.

"The truth is like ribbing," she said, switching to the philosophical mode of discourse she uses to end our conversations a winner. I looked at her to continue, to explain herself to this dense mind. "Just don't stretch it too far or it loses its shape," she said. She patted my shoulder, gave me a little kiss on the cheek, and went to check the calendar herself.

59. Three-Hour Dress

"Liar, liar," she said.

"Who me?" I asked.

"Not you," she said quickly. "The pattern company."

"The pattern company lied to you?" If she said so, the company was in trouble with her.

"It says so right on the package," she said. She showed me the package with the pattern for the dress she had just completed.

"It says 'petite' on the package. That's true. You are petite. Should the package have said 'tiny' or 'miniature'?"

"I'm not tiny, and I am not a miniature anything. That's not what's wrong."

I looked at the package again. I looked at the dress she had put on to see if it fit and how well it looked on her. It fit and it looked perfect, so I hugged her. "The dress matches the drawing on the package," I said. No lie there.

"The dress is fine. Keep looking," she said, and she pushed the package right up to my face. "Read what it says," she said.

I looked at the pattern number, the size, the company name, the bar code, the price. "They lied about the price?" I guessed. "You got it on sale, so the price is wrong."

"The prices are almost always wrong. All the stores sell the patterns at half-price as their regular price. Only in a real sale are the prices lower. I don't know why they play that game about prices, anyway. But that's not the lie," she said.

I looked carefully at the package. I turned it around, over, sideways, upside down. Finally there were only three words left to read. I read them aloud. "Three-Hour Dress."

"Liar, liar," my sweet Darling Wife yelled out. She took the package from my hand and shook it back and forth, then slammed it down hard on the cutting table.

"What should it have said?" I asked carefully, ready to jump out of her way immediately if she wanted to shake me or slam me down on the table.

"It should have said it was a three-day dress."

"It took you three days?"

"It took three hours just to get that flimsy pattern paper out of the package without tearing it. Then it took three more hours to iron out all the wrinkles. Then I had to cut it for my size. Then I had to cut out the fabric. And even then I wasn't ready to start sewing yet. I didn't get started until the second day. Reading the directions took a few minutes, but that's only because there weren't that many directions that made sense. So it took a half a day figuring out what the directions really meant and the other half of the day wondering what directions there should have been that were left out." She was out of breath.

"But you did figure it all out. The dress looks fine."

"I didn't figure out anything. When I began sewing, I kept getting confused and I had to keep going back to the pattern, and it took forever."

"But now it's all over and the dress is done," I said. I tried to calm her down, but there was still some frustration smoldering.

"Only because I gave up on the pattern and used some common sense," she said.

"You have a lot of common sense," I said. "You have a lot of sewing sense, too," I added. She reached for the pattern, her grip tight on it.

"Why don't you throw the pattern out?" I asked.

"I don't throw out patterns," she said. "I might need it some time again."

"Even if it's a slow pattern?" I asked.

"Three days isn't that slow," she said. "I once had a pattern for a jacket which took me a week to complete."

"And that made you angry, too?" I asked.

"No, I enjoyed making that jacket."

"But if it took a week…?"

"Sometimes it takes a long time."

"Then why weren't you angry?"

"The company didn't lie to me. The pattern package didn't say it was a three-hour jacket or even a three-day jacket."

"So you took your time?"

"I always take my time."

"Could anyone have made the dress you're wearing in three hours?"

"Maybe someone who didn't use the pattern." She seemed as if she were going to say more, but she paused and looked at the package she held tightly in her hand. She relaxed her grip and dropped the package onto the table. Then she went over to her box of marking pencils and markers and took a heavy-duty black felt marker out of the box. She uncapped it and ran a dark black line across the top of the package that held the pattern. She made several dark lines across the words "Three-Hour Dress." She then printed "Three-Day Dress" on the package.

"Truth in packaging," I said.

"At least it's not lying now," she said, as she put the package into a pattern box on the shelf next to the table. She turned back to me. "Do you really like this dress?" she said to me, turning herself around and around.

"Lovely," I said, and I was not lying.

60. A Wrinkle in Time

In her mother's house, washing and ironing day was on Monday. In our house it is as soon as the hamper is full. Years ago someone invented no-iron fabric, and life has been downhill ever since. Occasionally we find that something has to be ironed, but there never is a morning or afternoon or day assigned to that chore. That is why I couldn't believe it when she said, "Tomorrow's ironing day."

"What?" I asked, perplexed. Bewildered and bothered, as well. I hoped she didn't want me to join in. I had recently made the mistake of buying some quality sheets which were one hundred percent cotton. Untreated. That means they wrinkled. And wrinkled. And that meant, according to her thirty-fifth law (You bought it, you iron it!), I had to iron them. I do iron the pillowcases, but wrinkled sheets feel just fine.

"I have lots of ironing to do," she said, "and I've put it off long enough, and tomorrow's ironing day."

I thought little more about it, expecting that she had some clothes in the closet that had been hanging long enough to get wrinkled or have unwanted creases from the hangers. But this morning, I found out what ironing day meant.

"Getting ready to wrap presents already?" I was passing the room off the kitchen where we used to store food, but where she now stores mostly her stash and her patterns. She was at her cutting table surrounded by tissue paper.

"No," she said. "I told you yesterday I have ironing to do." She had large sheets of tissue in her hand, but I didn't see any presents. I thought the tissue was kind of bland-looking, some color of brown, but not quite tan. Also, it seemed to have lines on it.

"You're using old tissue to wrap the presents?" I asked. "We can still afford new tissue, even after your last trip to the fabric store."

"I'm not wrapping presents," she said. She picked up her iron and waved it at me. "I'm ironing."

"All right, if you say so," I said. I didn't believe her for one minute. I looked quickly around the small room for signs of wrinkled clothing, but I didn't see any. I knew it. She wanted to wrap *my* present and didn't want me to know. Oh, she was the clever one. But I didn't see any sign of any presents either.

She didn't accept my taunt but bent over her table and began to iron. But there was nothing in front of her except the wrinkled tissue. "All right, what *are* you ironing?" I asked. I was very curious indeed.

"I'm ironing my patterns."

"What?" I moved forward and looked more closely. And she was ironing a pattern.

"They wrap up the patterns so they are as wrinkled as they can make them," she explained, as I hung over her to see. She pushed me aside. "I have to iron them before I can use them. And I have a lot of them I plan to use in the next few weeks, so it will take all morning. Unless you want to help, go do something worthwhile." She already knew what I had to do. "Go outside and clean up the lawn, and out in the street, too."

That was it. She began ironing her patterns and I went out to clean up. When I came back half an hour later, she had taken a break from her ironing. She was wrapping the tissue paper patterns around the cardboard tubes she had saved from all the paper towel rolls we had used. She had about a hundred of them stored in a nook behind a cupboard. "I don't want the patterns to get wrinkled again," she said, answering me before I had even taken a breath to ask her what she was doing now.

"You don't have to tell me," I said, trying to save myself. "I know wrinkled patterns can be torture to use. Bless the invention of the iron," I said. "Iron on, Sweet Wife."

"How about if I iron out your old wrinkles?" she suggested, waving that iron again.

"I think I still have some cleaning up to do," I said. Wrinkles, my eye. Just last week she called me an old smoothie. Women!

61. A Mile Away Big

My mother, a professional dressmaker, a tailor, a natural seamstress, a patternmaker, had her own vocabulary when it came to sewing. Long after she passed away, I would catch myself using one of her words. In the years that my wife knew her as her mother-in-law, she too learned the vocabulary. So when my Darling Wife debated about which size she would use when she cut the pattern for a new hooded pullover shirt, she decided to follow common sense and go with medium. "All the T-shirts I wear are medium," she told me afterwards. "The shirt you bought me that I was trying to copy was medium," she tried to explain.

"You're a small," I said. "An extra small. That's X-small," I said. "You wear a petite size nothing," I continued, piling on the compliments.

"I just expected it to fit," she said. "Maybe the pattern runs large."

"And so it's not going to fit now?" I asked.

"It's going to be a mile away big," she said, as she held up the cut fabric pieces and prepared to sew them together into a shirt.

"That's mighty big," I said, not for a moment misunderstanding her measure of the shirt's size. Passed on down from generation to generation was the sewing vocabulary which could never be exactly defined, but that we both knew. Our children knew. Our grandchildren would soon know.

"If there could be just a bucketful too much salt in the soup," my mother used to say on sipping from a can of store-bought manufactured soup to explain why she wouldn't eat soup from a can, she could also explain that the sewing of a dress was finished when "there were enough stitches in it."

"But you're going to wear it?" I asked my Sweet Wife.

"Of course."

"Even if it would fit a mule?" I asked. I wasn't putting her down. In our vocabulary of clothing sizes, that was the description of a large garment.

"So it will hang a little," she said.

"It will hang below the floor," I said.

"Better a barn than a girdle," she said.

"Couldn't you take it in a tiny drop?" I asked. A large barrel would be more like it. After all, she could re-cut the fabric in a minute.

"A tuck here, a tuck there? Is that what you're asking?"

"It wouldn't hurt," I said.

"A person has to breathe," she said, as she went on with her sewing. She could also sew a sentence together when she had to.

By the next day she had a new hooded shirt. When she came to model it for me, the hood draped around both sides of her face and covered her eyes. The sleeves covered her arms and hands. The bottom hung nearly to her knees.

"Another tent for the circus," I said.

"You think it's too big, don't you? Be honest."

"The Goodyear Blimp is smaller."

"You're going to be smaller," she said.

"It was the pattern," I said, trying to rescue myself. "The pattern was made wrong." It was worth a try.

But she didn't bother to answer. She left me standing in place and swooshed out of the room, her shirt billowing. "Stay right there," she said, as she left the room. I stayed.

In two minutes she was back wearing another hooded-shirt. The same color. The same style. The same fabric. I could see her face. I could see her hands. I could see all of her. "Fits like a dream," I said. I don't know what that means exactly, but I know it's always the right thing to say to save one's life when confronted with the "What do you think?" look people have when they try something on.

"And what about the other one, the one that could house a wedding reception?"

"You mean my new hooded nightshirt?"

"New hooded nightshirt? Of course," I said quickly. I knew that, didn't I?

"So what about this one?" she asked, as she modeled her new shirt for me. "It's not too small is it?"

"Fits like an angel," I said. And I knew what I was talking about.

62. Fit for Charity

She promised she wouldn't sew Saturday morning so she could help me clean out the cabinets in the garage. I had already been working for two days to empty our lives of all the kitchenware, appliances, tools, and miscellaneous junk that had accumulated in our house over the years. The weather in the last two days had become cool enough to work in the garage, and though it would take her away from her sewing, she had finally agreed to help.

I had already filled several boxes and even more large shopping bags with the stuff I had planned to take to the Goodwill truck later that day. I had already attacked several of her storage places, but when she realized what I was doing, she let me know she had to pass on everything. "I have to look through it first. I might need some of it," she said. She didn't trust me do it my way, that is, to grab everything I saw and dump it into an outgoing bag or box. No, she wanted to be in charge.

Almost all of what she wanted to look through was clothing. While she went at it, I did another turn around the garage to see if I had missed anything. I stretched to reach the higher shelves and bent low to reach the lower shelves, looking through every inch of shadowy space to discover more old, musty, unused junk than I had imagined. Every few minutes I looked to watch her as she worked away, groaning and exclaiming over every piece of clothing she unpacked, looked over, and weighed carefully in her mind whether or not to discard it before finally giving it up. I knew each time she made the decision to toss a twenty-year-old skirt or a thirty-year-old vest into the charity pile, she did so with a tight heart. But she was courageous and, in her own way, ruthless.

Then I opened a gold cabinet that had been shoved up against the back wall of the garage, a cabinet that had been blocked before by boxes and one I had overlooked. I opened the doors and looked inside, and as I did so, I heard her screech. "I'll do that," she said in a voice she normally reserved for scaring this grown man into doing her bidding.

But she was on the other side of the garage, and her hands were full, so I started pulling out the piles of fabric that filled the cabinet. "What's this?" I said, as I held up a hooded scarf she had made during the summer when it was one hundred five degrees out. I recognized it immediately, for it was the first one she had ever made. "It's your scarf," I said.

"I know that," she said.

"So's this," I said, as I pulled out a second scarf. "And this," I said at the third scarf.

"I made three of them," she said.

"Only three?" I pulled out a fourth.

"All right, four," she admitted. She was holding two old jackets of mine I hadn't seen in years, and she quickly stuffed them into a giveaway bag before she came over to the cabinet. That took about one third of a second. She took the scarves away from me.

"What are your scarves doing in here?" I asked.

"Resting," she said.

"You don't plan to use them?" I asked.

"They're in storage."

"What kind of storage? Look at these other things," I said. I pulled out three blouses and two pairs of shorts.

"Storage for clothes I can't wear," she said.

"You can't wear these pants or this shirt?" I asked, as I dug deeper into the cabinet.

"All right, that's enough," she said. "They're all for charity."

"You made all these for charity?" I asked. Something was going on here.

"None of them were perfect when I made them, so I put them in the cabinet until I could get back to them. Are you satisfied?"

"And you never got back to them?"

"I have too many other things to sew."

"Will they fit other people?" I asked. I looked closely at the skirt I was holding. It looked fine to me.

"They'll all fit someone. They don't fit me or I didn't like the fabric or I just needed to learn on them. Some were just ideas I wanted to try that didn't work out."

"So it's all right to give them away?" She looked forlorn. I knew she didn't want to let go of them. She had so rarely made anything for herself. Just that morning she had told me she didn't need ever to make anything for herself again, that she had enough clothes to last until the twenty-third century.

"Yes," she said, sighing. She took the skirt from me and tossed it into an empty bag. "It's all right to give them away."

"You're absolutely certain?"

"Yes."

"You want to go through them all first?" Maybe she needed some time alone with them.

"Cold turkey," she said. "You do it. Toss them all. I enjoyed making them. I'll always have my memories."

"Do you want to watch?"

"No. Just do it. It's for charity," she said softly. Then she raised her voice back to its normal cheerful level. "I really have to go finish those matching shirts I'm making for the grandkids." She turned, took a deep breath, lifted her head high, and walked bravely away. But before she left the garage she turned and looked back one more time.

"Don't worry, I'll be kind," I said, as I began to pull the rest of the clothes out of the cabinet. And somehow, before I knew what had happened, I was working alone in the garage.

63. Top Ten

She was sitting at her machine, the light over her head casting her shadow down on the cotton squares she was turning into napkins. But she wasn't sewing. She was barely moving. I took the small dental mirror she uses to check the insides of her serger and held it up in front of her lips to see if she was breathing. She was, but barely.

"What is it?" I asked. This was not her normal position, frozen in place. She should have been humming along with her machine, turning out a dozen napkins with a woolly nylon rolled edge, her body in spirited animation.

"I've been thinking," she answered quietly.

"Thinking about what?" I asked in my best investigative manner.

"Why I sew," she said with a sigh.

"You've been sitting there in suspended animation wondering why you sew?" I asked. "You know why you sew. You sew for fun, for excitement, for the pleasure of providing your grandchildren with enough clothes to last them through school, college, their first marriages, and their successful careers."

"It's not always fun," she said.

"What do you mean it's not always fun?"

"Well, it's not fun when my metallic thread breaks eighty-seven times in a row or when my serger cuts off the sleeve of a blouse I'm sewing."

"Well, adventures happen. You've never complained before." Oh, she was frustrated at times, as when she discovered that her sewing machine wouldn't sew through eight layers of denim and make dinner at the same time. But she had always expressed happiness before. "What about all the other reasons you sew?"

"I've been thinking about that, how many reasons I really have for sewing." She seemed without emotion as she spoke. But her body moved slightly on her chair, and I did see her blink. She was definitely alive.

"How about ten reasons," I suggested. "Just try to come up with your top ten reasons for sewing. They have the top ten reasons for everything else on television. You can have them, too." I went to her desk and grabbed a pencil and a piece of paper. "I'll write them down for you," I said.

"But they may not be good reasons," she said. My wife the pessimist. She seemed a stranger to me.

"Don't be a pessimist," I said. "Give me one reason. We'll start with one reason."

"To avoid having to play the tuba," she said.

"What? You never played the tuba in your life. You're not taking this seriously, are you?"

"No, I just don't have any good reasons."

"How about pleasing your children and grandchildren?"

"I don't have to sew to do that. I can just send them money to buy clothes."

"It's not exactly the same. The labels won't say 'Made with Love by Grandma.' They'll say, 'Made by a Stranger in a Faraway Place by People Who Don't Even Know You.'"

"All right, but that's the only reason I sew."

"Is it? Is it really?" I said, feigning an angry rage, puffing out my cheeks and bellowing my words. "What about sewing because it's relaxing? Because it's creative? Because it's an adventure? Because it makes you smile? Because it keeps you from going out on the streets late at night selling drugs or breaking into stores or stealing hubcaps?"

"I don't do any of those things," she said, more animated now.

"Only because you are safe in this house sewing."

"So, what else, Mr. Know-It-All?" she asked. She even turned her head a few inches to look at me.

12 Months of Sewing

"So, what else is that you have the satisfaction of knowing how to adjust all four tensions on your serger. How many people do you meet who can do that?"

She looked stunned at the thought. "What else?" she said, softening.

"Saving money," I said, though I knew that was not true. We could buy out a whole children's section of any department store for what it cost her to make her two granddaughters a dress or her grandson a pair of shorts. I have three filing cabinets full of receipts just from fabric stores.

"Ha!"

"And you sew because otherwise I would be embarrassed at being out in public with buttons missing from my shirt or my pants having frayed cuffs."

"You can sew on buttons yourself and your pants don't have cuffs."

"Then how about the joy you felt when you learned to recognize and name four hundred colors of embroidery thread?"

"The names are on the spools," she said, but it was a feeble protest.

"No, they're not. Only the numbers. How many people besides you know that Number Three Hundred Eighty-Seven is peachy crimson with a lilac shadow?"

"I never liked that color," she said.

"And remember how much fun you had after you learned how to make a bib out of a hand towel, cutting the hole in the middle and sewing in the ribbing?"

"That was fun," she said.

"Even after you went berserk and made three hundred of them?"

"There are a lot of messy babies around," she replied seriously. "Why are you writing all this down?" she said, as she watched me scribbling furiously.

"Just taking a few notes," I said.

"What for?"

"Because people who don't sew always ask me why you sew. I never was sure before."

"Do you know why I sew now?" she said, as she stood away from her machine, went to one of her stacks of fabric, pulled down a large piece of burlap, and covered me in it. "I'll tell you why I'm going to sew right this moment," she said, as she pulled me toward the sewing machine. "And you can tell everybody the reason. You are a mad-man."

"Ooomph, mmmmm, owwww," was all I could say.

Popser Fans
From Around the World

"Thank you for seeing the lighter side of quilting and being so supportive."
Pat Rainey, Medina, Ohio

"I have to write to tell you how much my husband has enjoyed your column in *Quilt* magazine. He has the fortune (or misfortune?) to be married to a quilter and has seen all his tool storage space get smaller and smaller as my fabric collection gets bigger, and bigger—you know the story, I'm sure!

"We live in the north Highlands of Scotland, but some scenarios transcend boundaries. After I have had my fill of the rest of the magazine, he gets a chuckle out of you. It's nice to see that you are on-line and that he can catch up on all the columns he's missed. (I'm sure I'll hear about it: 'See, see, you're *all* psychopaths!')"
Sarah and Robert Henderson, Caithness, Scotland

"A quilting friend of mine gave me the link to your stories. Today I read the first two stories but I surely will return to get the others. It is a real pity that the English of my husband isn´t so well and he won´t be able to enjoy your writing, but 'fat quarter' he has learned finally. Thank you for these stories. I will enjoy the rest time by time."
Beate Vetter, Offenburg, Germany

"Haven't visited your website in a little while and was delighted to find six new columns. I've read (devoured) every one. You remind me of my husband and your wife reminds me of my mother, who died seven years ago. It's always a pleasure to read your words; they make me smile or even laugh out loud. Thank you for writing, and please don't stop. You bring quilting into my daily life, not just my evenings and weekends. (I guess that makes me a vampire quilter of sorts.) Enjoy!"
Judith B. Pritchett, Dallas, Texas

"I just returned from a Nordic Quilt Convention in Denmark myself and could really 'feel' your story about visiting a quilt show, getting pushed around in crowds, looking for my companion Monica! I am still looking through my good "Danish" quilting treasures from last weekend. Keep up the good stories!"
Hanne Reinertsen, Lorenskog, Norway

"I've just read your article and I've gotta tell you about the good time I had. From now on my husband is gonna call me DBQW (darling beginner quilting wife). Say hi to Joan."
Raquel Guimaraes Guedes, Foz do Iguassu, Brazil

Stories by Popser

Order Form

Additional copies of

12 Months of Sewing

are available from:

Open Chain Publishing
PO Box 2634-B
Menlo Park, CA 94026-2634
(650)366-4440 • fax (650)366-4455
www.thecreativemachine.com
e-mail: info@thecreativemachine.com

$15.95 plus shipping ($3.50 first book/$1 for each additional book)
(California residents add $1.32 state tax per book.)

Please send name, address, and phone (in case your order goes astray).
If the book is a gift, we will include a gift card from you.

Also available in *A Year in the Life* series:

52 Weeks of Quilting

Same price, same order address, same offer of a gift card.